WINDMILLS AT WORK
IN WEST SUSSEX

Compiled by JEM from the research
material of the late
MAURICE LAWSON FINCH

First published in 2006 by S. B. Publications
Tel: 01323 893498
Email: sbpublications@tiscali.co.uk

©2006 Eileen Finch

ISBN 1-85770-317-0

Cover picture
Shipley Mill, photographed by L. Woods

Designed and typeset by JEM Editorial, jemeditorial2@aol.com

CONTENTS

FOREWORD

This book is compiled from material about the windmills of Sussex collected by the late Maurice Lawson Finch over some fifty years, to which he added every picture postcard showing a windmill that he could find. He was a most assiduous collector of information and there can be few references to mills in newspapers, magazines and estate agents' property sales details that escaped his eagle eye from the end of the Second World War until his death in April 2000 at the age of seventy-five.

Maurice worked initially from maps dating from 1579 to the 1900s and he recorded all relevant information in respect of every mill on the forms he designed for the purpose.

With each form he filed photocopies of all published references he had obtained in respect of each mill together with all correspondence relating to it; often his own site plan – for he was a skilled draughtsman – and photographs, postcards and engravings. The material covering the mills of East Sussex filled seven box files, and he amassed four box files of material about the mills of West Sussex.

Maurice retired from his engineering business at Bishops Stortford in 1985 and moved with his wife, Eileen, and Simeon, the youngest of their three children, to Seaford. Previously his Sussex mill research had been confined to holiday visits to the county but he was now able to follow up every lead with visits to museums, libraries, art galleries and mill sites. He was often accompanied on his journeys of discovery by his uncle, Herbert Finch, an astronomer who moved to Hailsham in the 1940s when the Royal Observatory began its move to Herstmonceux Castle. Another companion was the late Gilbert Catt, last owner of Hamlin's smock mill at Hailsham, who retired in 1967 and later worked the watermill that had been restored by the Sussex Archaeological Society at Michelham Priory.

One result of the three mill-hunters' journeys around the county is a photographic record of the many mill conversions that have taken place - usually to private dwellings.

Maurice planned to write a book that would add the illustrations and information he had acquired to the extensive Sussex mill archive but he did not live to do so. In order that the material in those eleven box files was put to the use her late husband intended for it, Eileen commissioned two books in his memory – one for the windmills of East Sussex (published in 2004) and the second for the windmills of West Sussex.

Brigid Chapman
compiler of *Windmills at Work in East Sussex* (2004)

Capel Mill

HARNESSING THE WIND

Sussex was 'the greatest county of them all' for its windmills, according to Arthur Becket, who wrote: '... man never built anything more beautiful than a windmill, unless it is a sailing ship. One can hardly watch the sails of a windmill in motion without thinking of a sailing ship scudding before the wind. Both are animated figures in wide spaces; both suggest freedom; both, alas! have come to the time of their extinction ... the perfect English panorama must include both a windmill and a sailing ship.'

The stiff, prevailing south-westerlies may have had something to do with the prevalence of windmills in Sussex (it has been estimated that some 900 worked in the county over 800 years); many were built right on the coast to take advantage of bracing breezes straight off the sea – and as many were built high on the Downs. The wind that worked the windmills was also, in dozens of cases, responsible for their destruction. Erected on open or high ground, the mills were exposed to the full fury of the storms and gales that blew them down.

From antiquity corn has been ground between two stones to produce flour and thus the bread of life. The first mills were querns, small hand-mills consisting of two circular flat stones, the upper one, pierced with a central hole/eye, pivotted and revolving on a wooden or metal pin inserted in the lower stone. Then came watermills, supposedly introduced to England in the ninth century – but possibly dating from Roman times. These were of use only where there was a suitable source of water such as a river, a swift-flowing stream or the sea tide. Three centuries passed before an alternative means of grinding corn became available.

The windmill, which used a mechanical means of harnessing the power of the wind to turn the stones, was already in widespread use across Europe and in the Middle East in mediaeval times and was brought here, some say, by the Crusaders in the twelfth century.

There are three types of windmill, each unique in its own right –

the post and socket mill, the smock mill and the tower mill. The oldest and simplest is the post mill, the body of which revolved upon a central post, occasionally a large tree, sunk into the ground and supported by a massive wooden trestle. Later it was found useful to enclose the trestle on which the mill was supported, to create the roundhouse, which became a handy store room. The sweeps – originally cloth sails rigged to spoked frames – were attached to a wooden or metal windshaft, angled between 10° to 15° to the horizontal and carrying a wooden toothed gear wheel which drove the horizontal millstones by means of a pinion. The sweeps were turned into the wind at first by ropes, then by a pole, fixed to the rear of the mill body, that was moved around manually. Later post mills were equipped with a fan-tail or vane which brought the mill into the wind automatically.

An example of an early post mill showing the pole by which it was turned into the wind; the timbers of the supporting trestle were later walled in to form the roundhouse

Smock mills, a sixteenth century Flemish invention, were introduced into England in the eighteenth century and gained their name from a supposed resemblance to a countryman in his round-frock. The advantage of the smock mill was that, unlike the post mill, the body did not have to be moved to bring the sweeps into the wind because they were fixed to a rotating cap that carried the wind-shaft. This cap was turned by hand or chain in older mills, and later by fan tackle which turned the sweeps into the wind automatically.

The tower mill, the final evolution of the windmill, was a tall round brick or stone structure with its sweeps on a cap at the top. This cap revolved on a metal ring and the sweeps were turned head to wind by the fantail at the rear. The motion which the rotating sweeps communicated to the axis was transferred to a central shaft running

A typical smock mill with its octagonal wooden studding

from top to bottom of the mill by means of bevelled gears. Cog-wheels fixed to the shaft engaged the millstones and secondary machinery such as hoists, dressers, cleaning machines and oat rollers.

In 1745 Edmund Lee patented the device whereby sweeps were moved into the wind automatically. He placed a fan at the back of a rotating cap at right-angles to the sweeps and this remained stationary as long as the sweeps were facing the wind. If there were a change of wind direction, the fan, which was geared to the rack round the curb, turned it to bring the sweeps back into the wind.

Another improvement in the eighteenth century was Meikle's invention of the spring sweep. Instead of a canvas cover, which the miller had to adjust by climbing on to the framework, this had a number of hinged shutters connected by a spring-loaded bar by which they could be opened or closed manually. In 1807 William Cubitt produced his patent sweep, the shutters of which could be adjusted mechanically through a system of levers and weights without stopping the mill.

Two main types of

This derelict tower mill (Halnaker) shows the rack which was fixed round the metal ring or curb on which the cap turned; attached to it is the wooden frame that held the fan

millstone were used, the French burr and the peak. The first, used mainly for grinding wheat for flour, was made from shaped segments of a fresh-water quartz found in the Seine valley, bound together in iron hoops. A French burr stone could be up to 4ft 6in diameter and weigh up to 17cwt. The other type was a hard sandstone from the peak district of England. Peak stones were used mainly for grinding barley, oats and maize.

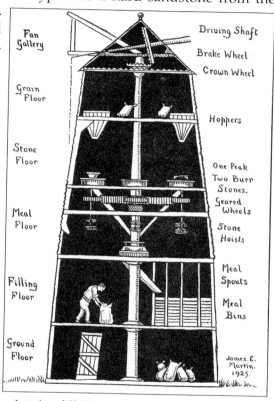

Only the upper stone, the runner, revolved, the lower, or bedstone, being fixed. The stones did not touch each other, rather being arranged a 'hair's breadth' apart, grinding taking place between the radial and tangential furrows and grooves in the stone faces. The direction of the radial pattern was such that the grain was eased outwards across the face of the stone.

By the eighteenth century there were windmills in most towns and villages in Sussex. In 1813, when the first Ordnance Survey sheets

Interior of Shipley Mill showing the workings of a windmill: drawing by James E Martin 1925

covering the county were published, 153 sites were marked, almost every one occupied by a working windmill.

Today, the standing windmills (including conversions) in West Sussex are South Marsh Mill at Arundel; Barnham Tower Mill; Jack and Jill at Clayton; Climping Mill; Earnley Mill; East Wittering Mill; Halnaker Mill; High Salvington Mill; Nutbourne Mill;

Nyetimber Mill; Medmerry Mill at Selsey; Shipley Mill; Rock Windmill at Washington and West Chiltington Mill. Mills that have not been converted to private homes, and that may be visited are open to view on National Mills Day, usually the second Sunday in May, and on Sundays and perhaps a weekday from April to September. The Sussex Mills Group, formed to promote the study and restoration of mills, issues a leaflet giving full details of the individual mills and their opening times. It is available from Tourist Information Centres, from participating mills, also from D H Cox, 3 Middle Road, Partridge Green, Horsham, West Sussex RH13 8JA, telephone 01403 711137. The group's website is: www.sussexmillsgroup.org.uk

JEM

Aldingbourne

There were once two windmills serving this village, which was among the original endowments of the Saxon See of Selsey, founded in AD709. Bishops of Chichester had an episcopal mansion in the parish in the early Middle Ages.

The Old Black Mill (West Mill, SU937072) was first recorded in 1719 and was 'pulled down' after 1861. At some time before the first one-inch Ordnance Survey of 1813 it was joined by the White Mill (East Mill, SU937071), which stood three-quarters of a mile to the east. This mill was also pulled down after 1861.

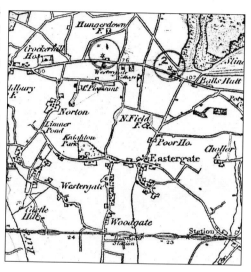

The two windmills (circled by MLF) are clearly marked on the first edition of the OS map of 1813

Amberley

There was a windmill about half a mile south of the church of St Michael in the early eighteenth century. It was succeeded by one on the same site (TQ029122) shown on the 1876 six-inch OS sheet near what is now Mill Lane. In the mid-thirteenth century Pope Urban IV assumed the Protection of the Church of Chichester and forbade

Watercolour of Angmering Post Mill by Wilfrid Ball

'rape, theft, arson, blood-letting, imprisonment, killing or violence' within the confines of a mill at Amberley – and another at Angmering.

Angmering Post Mill seen working early in the twentieth century

Angmering

Little remains today of the three windmills and a water pumping mill that once served Angmering – a village whose name derived from Angemaer's people, a tribe that built a settlement on the site of a Roman villa. The coastal resort of Angmering-on-Sea was built between the two world wars.

A post mill (TQ072041), thought to have been built in 1730, was called Luck's Mill, after the last owner, Frederick Luck. The mill was brought from Arundel early in the eighteenth century and stood sentinel to the east end of the community, at what is now Mill Road, for more than 200 years. The post on which it turned was thought to be a whole oak tree, roughly shaped to three feet square. Mr Luck converted to steam in 1899, but the canvas-covered sweeps were not removed until 1914 or 1915 when it was feared the mill could be a landmark for the enemy during the Great War. It's said the sawn-off sweeps, which used to drive a pair of peaks and a pair of burrs, were used for firewood.

Angmering Post Mill in 1930

For the next twenty-five years the mill was worked by Frederick Luck's son – first by a coal-fired engine, and later by a petrol engine. The black-tarred upper part, which by now had become very derelict, was removed in 1930, leaving only the round-house. Windmill enthusiast Thurston Hopkins described this in the 1920s as:

The roundhouse: MLF 1981

One of the most picturesque in Sussex, for its brickwork is full of delightful irregularity, and here and there it bulges like an elderly gentleman growing a paunch – the whole building being held together in a cohesive unity by a coat of lumpy tar.

A portion of the 1813 OS map shows Luck's Mill (1) and Jerusalem Mill (2)

Jerusalem Mill (TQ068040), sited close to Luck's Mill at the eastern end of the village, was a late eighteenth century post mill erected off what is now Station Road. It is believed that the mill was moved to Rustington *c*1850, where it became Bridge Mill.

On a track leading from the village to

Highdown Hill are to be found the remains of Highdown New Mill, or Ecclesden Mill (TQ082044) named for nearby Ecclesden Manor. It was a fine tower mill with beehive cap, a large set of patent sweeps and a sturdy mill house.

The mill, which worked two pairs of stones (one peak, the other French burr) was built in 1826 for Henry Grant who, with his family, worked the mill for the whole of its short commercial life – which ended in 1872.

The cap and sweeps had blown off and their remains thrown into a nearby chalk pit. By the 1930s the wreck had deteriorated to a creeper-clad curiosity. It was described as looking like an

Highdown New Mill after its conversion into part of a private house: MLF 1981

unusually squat, ivy-covered tree. In the 1970s the shell of the tower was restored and incorporated into a new bungalow that was offered for sale three years later for £50,000.

In June 1994 Highdown New Mill, now called Mill House, was put on the market for £400,000. This was after failing to sell for £349,000 six months earlier. The Daily Telegraph of June 15 (above) described the property as a large bungalow with eight bedrooms, swimming pool, stabling, paddock and views over Downs and sea.

14

The pumping mill on a mezzotint postcard of 1904   *In 1937:* C S Harding

Angmering also had an unusual pumping mill at Preston Place Farm. It was mounted on top of a barn and instead of the usual sweeps, it had a circular wooden wheel. The structure was built in 1853 for a man called Warren and considered a great curiosity in its day. Power was transmitted to three machines – a water pump, a turnip chopper and a corn mill. The wheel worked successfully for around seventy years. It ceased during the Second World War and was removed. The tower and the farm buildings remained for some years afterwards but eventually were lost to development.

Apuldram/Appledram

Overlooking Dell Quay on Chichester Harbour is a striking white house that has a conically-capped roundel wing to the side. Were this in East Sussex it could be assumed to be a converted oast house. In fact it contains the remains of Dell Quay Windmill (SU835029).

The roundhouse as a single-storey wing

In 1790 (the earliest reference to a mill at Apuldram) this mill was insured for £200. Eight years later the church register contains this brief observation:

15

Thomas Pearce killed by the windmill.

Who was Thomas Pearce – the miller? Perhaps a mill-worker? And how was he killed?

Dell Quay windmill was a large square-built post mill which had two pairs of stones and was described in sale particulars of 1807 and 1810 as capable of grinding seven loads a week. It was then owned by a William Wild.

As this early mill was not recorded on the first edition of the Ordnance Survey map of 1813, it may be that it had become derelict, or burned down and a

Dell Quay House with a second storey added to the roundhouse: MLF 1988

replacement was put up by 1823, when it was recorded on the Greenwoods' map of 1825.

Dell Quay Mill was worked until about 1870 when it was dismantled, leaving just the brick roundhouse. Originally this was thatched and became an outbuilding. It was integrated into Dell Quay House in 1948, first as a single storey addition. Later a second storey was added together with a conical, tiled roof.

Arundel

In the nineteenth century Arundel had three working windmills on the south bank of the Arun. Before the railway arrived, sailing barges came up the river to trade, bringing coal and other necessities and taking away the product of the mills.

South Marsh Mill (TQ013063), half a mile south of Arundel Bridge, was a black tower mill with fantail and beehive cap, built in 1830. The five-storied mill worked three pairs of underdrift stones, one of peaks, two of burrs. The first occupants were Henry Dendy and Michael Pellet, who worked the mill until 1837; Pellet ran it alone until 1841 when the Bartlett family took over. In 1915 a ferocious storm caused serious damage to the sweeps and windshaft, and the mill ceased to be wind-powered. It continued with an alternative power unit until 1921.

A design fault – in which the windows were placed one above the other – formed a natural fracture line that may have contributed to distortion of the curb on which the cap rotated and in 1936 a mock-up cap was set on top of the sweep-less tower. Early in the Second World War the iron mill machinery was removed to further the war effort and the structure was converted to a private house.

Arundel's Cement Mill (TQ023067) has been described as both a post mill

The tower minus sweeps and beehive cap as it was in 1936

South Marsh Mill, c1912

17

Detail from an oil by L A Wilcox, c1870,
Topsail Schooners at the Port of Arundel

and a tower mill, although almost certainly it was a post mill, the earliest reference to it being 1778. It stood on the bank of the river, a quarter of a mile south-east of the bridge. As its name suggests, it was used to grind cement which was hauled away by barge. The mill was last shown marked in 1824 and was demolished at an unknown date.

Attfield's Mill was first noted on the map of 1875-6. It, too, was a quarter of a mile south-east of the bridge, putting it alongside the cement mill.

The Old Post Mill at Arundel, shown on maps from 1724 to 1795, possibly known as Badsworth Mill, was located just south-east of the town bridge. This was the mill that was later removed to Angmering some time before 1813.

Ashington

Windmill Close, off Rectory Lane in Ashington, is the only reminder of a windmill marked on maps from 1780 to 1817 on a site approximately three-quarters of a mile north-north-east of Ashington church.

Ashurst

All that remain now of Ashurst Mill (TQ181160) are a section of its centre post converted to a garden ornament, a peak runner stone and a French burr bed stone. The burr was inserted into a conservatory floor at Old Mill House, which was built in 1952 using bricks from the great piers that supported the mill.

This was an open trestle post mill, built in 1789, that worked for some 112 years. It was a small two-storey structure, supported on a wooden trestle resting on four solid brick piers, and reached by twenty-six steps.

Thurston Hopkins wrote of it in 1927:

> Ashurst Mill, a battered old ruffian, leaning on his timber supports, has somehow managed to defy wind and rain even up to the present day. It seems an extraordinary thing that this particular mill should have

Ashurst Mill

> weathered the storm so long, for being built up on brick piers, about 12 feet high, it stands in a much more perilous position than other mills. It is in such a decayed state that it is likely to collapse under any sudden strain.

Windmill enthusiasts urged the owner to have the old mill repaired, but he was not interested in doing so. By 1928 the mill was badly battered, stripped of much of its weatherboarding, exposed to the elements and had a sweep missing. The great gale of December 1929 felled what was said to be 'the most picturesque mill in the county'.

From the Worthing Herald, July 31, 1925, No 19 in the series Sussex Curiosities – A Fallen Landmark

19

Barnham

There were three windmills here – on what was claimed to be the best corn-growing land in Sussex. The oldest, Feaver's Post Mill, was marked on maps from 1724 to 1823, and sited about two-thirds of a mile north-east of the parish church. In 1823 it was moved to Fishbourne.

Drawing (from about 1700) of Feaver's Post Mill

The site of a second post mill (SU968038), a little to the south of Feaver's Mill, was marked on only one map, that of 1780. It was said to have fallen down in October 1827.

In this same position (on the south of what is now Yapton Road) a

Barnham Tower Mill pictured for a J White postcard early in the 20th century

tower mill was built by John Baker – in 1790 according to one of its millers – and perhaps the two stood side by side for some thirty-seven years, although no records of this have been found. It seems more likely that the tower mill was built, as a replacement for the second post mill, in 1829 as it was put up for sale on January 23 in 1830 and advertised in the *Brighton Herald* as 'this substantially-built cylindrical mill recently built without regard to expense'.

Barnham minus its sweeps: MLF 1983

Maurice Finch spent Friday, May 6, 1983, with a Mr R C Reynolds at Barnham Tower Mill. Seventy-seven-year-old Mr Reynolds, a nephew of John Baker, in whose family the mill had been since 1880, believed that the mill was built in 1802/3 rather than the 1790 date claimed by his uncle, as did local writer G M Fowell, but Maurice's researches found no evidence of this. The Feaver family which, in 1830, had been milling in the village for more than 100 years, worked the tower mill until it was sold to the Baker family.

Firebox from the steam engine that once drove the tower mill: MLF 1983

Whatever its age, the flint and stone-built tower mill, with its black body and white shutterless sweeps, fantail and stage, was run by wind-power until some time in the 1920s when the machinery was converted for use by a gas engine. The sweeps were removed shortly afterwards to lessen wind resistance.

The mill has four floors, two pairs of stones, a roller flour mill, grain cleaners and kibbling machinery – and bells attached to the feeding spouts to warn the miller when the hoppers were empty.

John Baker's son, also John, said:

'When my father was working this mill he could count eleven other windmills working from this platform. But now they have all vanished. Halnaker Windmill can just be discerned on the skyline over towards Stane Street. That was built in the time of Queen Anne, but it has been nothing but a wingless ruin for the last hundred years.'

The mill was still being worked by the Baker family in the early 1980s, producing poultry foods and pig meal by electric rather than wind- or steam-power. In 1989 it was bought by Victor May who intended to restore it to a working windmill, but nothing came of this plan and the mill was sold again, in a dilapidated state, in 1994.

Now restoration has recommenced it is hoped that Barnham tower mill will once again work by wind power and will grind the corn to make the bread served in the tearoom that has opened in an old stable. The mill and tearoom are open all year, Tuesday to Sunday, and bank holidays, 10am to 5.30pm. Entry is by donation.

Beeding

A post mill at Beeding, built during the latter half of the eighteenth century, stood on Windmill Hill alongside the track from Golding Barn to Castletown. It was worked by a Harry Slaughter until 1828 and sold by auction at the White Lion Inn, Steyning, on May 29 that year to a man named Irish, who carried out much restoration work the following year. Subsequent millers were Richard Hugh Kidd, Hugh Bright and finally R Filley. The mill ceased working around 1870, was derelict by 1876 and was blown down in a gale c1888.

At the time of the threatened French invasions of 1778 and 1779, the mill was ordered to be held as a fortified post.

Billingshurst

Sprink's Mill stood on a hill behind the sixteenth century Six Bells Inn – now Ye Olde Six Bells – in this old coaching town on Stane Street until it burned down on November 5, 1852. Sussex being famous for its bonfire tradition, could this mill have been the victim of an over-enthusiastic celebration of the Fifth?

It was a post mill, dating from the end of the eighteenth century.

Ruin of Hammond's smock mill:
MLF 1983

The village also had a smock mill, known as Hammond's Mill (TQ092261). Built in 1825, according to a diamond-shaped stone over its door, this stood on a two-storey base of the local standstone a quarter of a mile north-east of the church. It was built for Richard Chennell by J Streeter.

The mill was badly damaged in the Shrove Tuesday gale of 1906. In 1920 the unsafe remains of the smock were burned down leaving only the ruins of the octagonal roundhouse, which today are engulfed by foliage.

Birdham

Birdham Old Mill, just east of the parish church, was a post mill that was worked from early in the eighteenth century until 1779, when it was blown down. A second mill (SU830001) replaced it and this was gone by 1840. Birdham also once had a pumping mill in the form of a small, black smock with short white sweeps. Built in 1935, it was used to raise water via a crank and pump for a local farmer but within four years it ceased to work and the smock was allowed to deteriorate. It had vanished within a decade.

Bognor

Nothing remains today of the town's three windmills – East Mill, near

Black Mill at Bognor 1899

the eastern end of the Promenade, Shripney Mill in the South Bersted area and Black Mill on the Aldwick side of town.

The first, almost certainly a post mill, was recorded in a terrier of land in private ownership as early as March 10, 1626, as having long since disappeared and that its site had been washed away by the sea. The second, also a post mill, was known to have existed from 1724 and was blown down in 1779. It may have been the mill marked on a 1909 Ward Lock plan of Bognor, off Neville Road, although Maurice found a reference to Shripney Mill being a little over half a mile north-east of South Bersted church.

Black Mill was put up in the 1820s by William Attfield to grind cement, it then being the fashion to cement-render homes in imitation of John Nash's stucco houses in the capital.

In 1880 the mill was converted by Thomas Norris for the production of flour, but worked for only a few years before being demolished at the turn of the nineteenth and twentieth centuries. This windmill, which stood near the sea at Aldwick, was not marked on maps, but was listed in the 1851 Census.

Bolney

Long gone is the post mill shown on the 1795 Yeakell and Gardner map half a mile north of the thirteenth century parish church. Gone, too, is Bolney Mill (TQ264234), a smock dating from the mid-nineteenth century. It had ceased grinding by 1905, for a pair of its

.As it was.

As it is   a Bolney Windmill ? The old miller.

stones form part of the traditional lych gate made of Sussex oak and marble that Edward Huth gave to St Mary's church that year. It was demolished in 1916.

Boxgrove

One of the county's earliest windmills, a simple post mill, shown on maps and in parish records from 1595, stood beside the Roman Stane Street, a mile and a half north-north-east of Boxgrove Priory church. The last mention of it was in 1779.

And one of Sussex's best known mills, Halnaker (SU920097), was also built in the parish. This was an early tower mill, set on a site close to the ancient mill, supposedly in the reign of Queen Anne (1702-14), although the first map to mark it was that of 1795. It stands today on high ground near Goodwood and is a well-loved landmark in West Sussex – not least for pilots using Ford airfield. It is believed that a windmill stood on this same hill as far back as 1540, and that the present tower was put up in 1740. A Halnaker mill, built for the Duke of Richmond and the Goodwood estate, has stood on this site for centuries, but the small tower now there is dated c1750 by Brunnarius. Whatever the date, it is certainly the oldest tower mill

Halnaker Mill, derelict, pictured on
an Austin postcard of 1913, above;
and restored, left, pictured
on May 4, 1983: MLF

still standing in Sussex, and is the windmill immortalised by Hilaire Belloc in his poem *Ha'nacker Mill*.

The name Halnaker, from the Old English *healf an aecer*, meaning 'half a strip of cultivated land', became 'half-naked' in 1274, and then Halnaker, pronounced 'Hannacker'.

*Halnaker in ruins, 'the fan-wheel looking
for all the world like a rifle on its shoulder'*

The mill has a four-foot thick wall at its base and was tile-clad. In use, the four sweeps were covered with canvas and the mill ran two pairs of overdrift stones. In 1905 it was struck by lightning which split the wooden windshaft and damaged the cap. The then owner was G R Watkins, who had worked the mill for thirty years; his father and his grandfather were millers there before him. Watkins failed to repair the windmill and gradually it fell into a ruinous condition.

James Martin, in *Old English Mills and Inns*, wrote:

> On the apex of the cone-shaped Halnaker Hill stands the ruined shell of a fine old mill; bearing itself erect like a sentinel, in its fine coat of red-burnt tiles, with the beams of the ruined fan-wheel looking for all the world like a rifle on its shoulder.

In 1934 Halnaker Mill was acquired by Sir William Bird, a former High Sheriff of Sussex, and a JP, who lived at Eartham. He employed Neve's of Heathfield to restore the mill as a memorial to his late wife. New common sweep frames were fitted to the iron windshaft and brake wheel taken from Punnett Town's smock mill and a sixteen-

UGUST 30 1985   **THE TIMES**

Plastic bonnet for the old mil.

Halnaker Windmill a 200-year-old West Sussex landmark undergoing tests during a facelift.

The work has been undertaken by the Bognor Regis-based firm Sussex Renovations. Mr Graham Benge, Contracts Manager (left) i-

with a liquid plastic material to arr further deterioration, but it will still like the present canvas covering.

Halnaker is a tower mill which, unus for this type, does not turn, as it face prevailing wind. It has been restored before

Cutting from The Times of Friday, August 30, 1985, showing continuing restoration

27

sided beehive cap was placed on the empty tower, which had its windows bricked in and the outer covering of the red tiles reinstated.

Maurice copied two plaques when he visited Halnaker on May 4, 1983. The first was on the outside above the door lintel and read:

> This ancient landmark was restored in the year 1934 by Sir William Bird of Eartham in memory of his wife.

The second, on the back inside wall, was defaced and difficult to read, but Maurice was able to record the following:

> This mill was restored by H E Waters Ltd of Forest Row
> E W Neve of Heathfield
> Rex Wailes Engineer
> J C Coles Estate Steward
> Employed were J Beedle of Hemsley, A Scott, E Theobald, J Clarke, O Codley

Later in the 1980s further restoration work was carried out at Halnaker and a plastic bonnet was fitted. Halnaker Mill is open all year; there is no admission charge.

Bramber

Earliest references to a mill here were in 1778 and 1779 when, like Beeding Mill, it was chosen to be fortified against a Napoleonic invasion. Nothing remains.

Burgess Hill

The town that has grown up round St John's Common has not forgotten its windmill, known as Wood's Mill, for today it has a Mill Road, a Windmill Drive, a Millbank, a Miller's Way and a Mill Wood. The mill stood near the church of St John the Evangelist (TQ314196) from at least 1823 when it was first noted, until 1861 when Mill Road (formerly Windmill Lane) was, on June 2, 'dedicated to the use of the public'.

Capel

The fine octagonal smock, Kingsfold Mill at Capel, with its massive hooded cupola, was also known as Shiremark Mill as it stood exactly on the boundary of Sussex and Surrey. It has been claimed as a Surrey mill, but Hilaire Belloc in *The Four Men* declared it to be in Sussex. He wrote:

> When the Last Judgement comes the whole world will be wiped out, but Sussex will be preserved for the faithful as a garden of paradise, and the chosen ones will have to run the gauntlet of Shiremark Mill where the Angel with the Flaming Sword will stand in authority.

Kingsfold's sweeps were turned to the wind by pulling on chains that hung down from beneath the rear of

Kingsfold/Shiremark Mill
Collector card c1928

the hooded cap, marking it as one of the earliest designs of smock mill as this type of mechanism was superseded in 1745 when the fantail was invented.

The mill's sweeps were of the Sussex type, consisting of many shutters that could be opened and closed like a venetian blind to regulate wind pressure. The Surrey sail is of a different pattern and has much wider shuttering.

1948

29

The picturesque mill was restored by its then owner, Captain E Broadwood, in the 1920s. But in the years that followed it was again neglected, fell into disrepair and stood derelict for many years in a dense thicket until destroyed by fire in October 1972. Arson was suspected.

Chichester

Portfield Smock Mill in Oving Road, Chichester

Over the centuries six mills served Chichester. St James's Post Mill stood three-quarters of a mile north-east of the Market Cross from 1724 and the 1813 OS map shows it replaced by a smock mill on the same site (SU872053). Then there was Broyle Mill (SU861060) and Old Broyle Mill (SU858058), both last recorded in 1824, and both a quarter of a mile or so north of St Paul's church.

Portfield Post Mill, dating from the very early years of the eighteenth century, was a mile east of Chichester Cross and was replaced a century later by Portfield Smock Mill (SU877047). This, too, has gone, pulled down in May 1905.

Clayton

The Jack and Jill windmills standing side by side on the top of Duncton Down (or Clayton Hill as it is better known today,) a few miles north of Brighton, have long been a famous Sussex landmark. Cobbett said of them that:

> ... they are so admirably sited on the crest of the Down as to be

almost as important in the landscape as the ring on Chanctonbury's head.

The roundhouse of Duncton Mill: MLF 1982

Less well known was Duncton Mill, which preceded the picturesque twins. Its roundhouse remains as part of Jack's living quarters.

Duncton (TQ304134), built in the second half of the eighteenth century, was joined in the early 1850s by Jill (TQ303134), a white post mill that had been built in 1821 near what is now the Seven Dials in Brighton, on the road to Devil's Dyke. Here it stood above what was to become the Belmont railway tunnel. Clayton miller, James Mitchell, bought Lashmar's Mill, as Jill then was, and had her pulled on a trolley sledge drawn by teams of horses and oxen over the Downs to Clayton to join Duncton Mill.

Jack and Jill photographed in 1909 for a Homewood postcard

Both Jack and Jill ceased working in 1907 when the last owner, a Mr Wood, found that business could not support their upkeep. A year later a storm damaged the fan machinery by which Jill was turned to face the wind and the body was filled with chalk to act as ballast and stop it swinging about. Jill fell into decay over the next few decades until, in 1953, it was renovated by millwright Ernest Hole of Burgess Hill on behalf of the then Cuckfield Rural District Council. Later the mill passed into the care of Mid Sussex District Council and now is looked after by the Jack and Jill Windmills Society.

Jack and Jill: G N Ridal

Jill is open on National Mills Day, Sundays and bank holidays from May to September, 2-5pm. Entry is by donation.

The five-storey black tower mill, Jack (TQ304134), was built against Duncton Mill's roundhouse in 1866 to replace the older mill, and a door was opened between the two. Jack worked three pairs of underdrift stones and had a power take-off in the spout floor. The stones were one pair of peaks and two of burrs.

Millstones let into the ground at the entrance to Jack: MLF 1982

For Jack, owner Charles Hammond patented a new method of sweep control in 1873. This consisted of a centrifugal governor that varied the speed of the double-shuttered sweeps from a pre-determined optimum. The shutters were automatically opened through the striking gear, thus the miller could rely on sweep speed rather than

32

varying wind pressure.

Three pairs of stones were laid out as a path to the mill after it ceased working in 1907. The tower was then partially gutted and fitted out as a holiday home. It was rented during the summers of 1908, 1909 and 1910 by archaeologist Edward Martin while he studied Sussex dewponds.

In 1909 the revolving cap was fixed and in a storm shortly afterwards the fan broke loose and rolled down the hill. At the same time two of the sweeps broke off. The remaining sweeps were removed later.

In 1911 the Anson family took up residence, had the remaining machinery removed, and stayed for some forty years. Later residents were writer and golfing correspondent Henry Longhurst and his wife Claudine, who lived in Jack from 1953 until Henry's death in 1978.

In 1973 a film company paid £3,000 to use Jack as the star of the film *The Black Windmill*, and for this purpose Peter Stenning of Edwin Hole's firm made a new set of sweeps for the windmill before it faced the cameras.

Clymping

Known variously as Clymping, Climping, Tottisham and Cuttleworth – and in the 1920s as Atherington – Clymping Mill (TQ015012) was a venerable old smock, dating from the turn of the nineteenth century, that succumbed to deathwatch beetle and was cut down to be converted into part of a house. The two-storey remains are actually in Atherington village, a mile south-east of Climping church.

There had been a mill at 'Mill Feylde' in Clymping since at least 1606, when one was marked on a map of that date. This was succeeded by Cuttleworth Mill, which was

Clymping Mill in a state of dereliction

seen on an Admiralty map of 1698.

A William Challen offered for sale a black mill on the same site in 1796. The buyer pulled it down and put up a new smock mill there – the Bailiffscourt estate – in 1799. Mounted on a single-storey base of knapped flints, brick and stone, it had a black beehive cap and carried spring sweeps that worked two pairs of stones. The mill, once owned by Christ's Hospital, was used until 1899, after which it stood derelict

and unoccupied. In 1919 Sir Richard Garton bought it, most of the internal machinery was removed and the mill was incorporated into a newly-built house. Fixed, dummy sweeps were fitted to replace the originals. The millstones became garden ornaments. In 1952 the property was sold to a Mr T Bage, and two years later it once again became part of the Bailiffscourt estate.

The cut down mill formed part of a school: MLF

All was well until 1962 when death-watch beetle was found in the timbers and it was necessary to reduce the main structure to just two storeys. A *Daily Telegraph* report of August 4, 1969, said the Sussex Industrial Architecture Group was opposing a plan by the Marchioness of Normanby, who then owned it, to 'knock down Tottisham Mill and use the site for farming'. Kim Leslie, the group's secretary, said: 'Tottisham is one of the earliest smock windmills in Sussex on an unspoiled part of the coast. While the machinery and the sails have been removed, the building itself is an historic visual amenity which we feel should be preserved.' He added that as the mill covered only half an acre, he failed to see how farming the land could be an economic proposition.

At the time the mill was leased to the Reverend Kenneth Oliver, a former army padre, who ran it as a tutorial establishment for thirty-five teenage boys. His lease was due to run out.

Because of the opposition, plans to demolish the mill were dropped

Coolham Mill, above, in a 1926 book and left, after the loss of its spring shutters

and the building came under the protection of The National Trust. In 1973 it was offered for sale by private treaty and bought by the Post Office for its pensions fund. It later formed part of Mill School.

Coolham

Coolham or Bailey Mill (TQ115233) was an old post mill seen on maps between 1813 and 1920. It was moved to the locality from Kirdford in 1800. The post on which it turned was cut in Hoes Wood, two miles away at Shipley. A *Sussex County Magazine* correspondent, G E Naldrett of Horsham, wrote in 1930:

> My father used both the watermill and the windmill at Bailey's Farm. My brother and I assisted him after I left school. My father was the last man to use the windmill ... the windmill was similar to that at Bodle Street Green. I have two postcards of it showing two cloth sweeps, for which I cut the last sail cloths. The other two sweeps were spring shutters, one of which blew off one Ash Wednesday. My father was grinding at the time, consequently we had to remove the

other sweep, and grind with two thereafter.

The mill was pulled down in 1919 and its timbers were used to make furniture for the Knepp Castle estate offices.

Compton

Compton Mill (TQ782146), built a quarter of a mile south-east of the parish church, was a post mill dating from early in the eighteenth century. It was worked for at least one hundred years before vanishing from the landscape.

Cuckfield

There were three mills at Cuckfield two of which were post mills, both known as Whiteman's Green Mill. The earlier was also called

Whiteman's Green Smock Mill during its working life

Mill entrance: MLF 1983

Kennard's Mill. The latter would have been the mill known to have been pulled down some time in the 1870s after years as a forsaken derelict. It stood, apparently, in a field called Stroods, south of the London road.

There is mention of Whiteman's Green Mill, whether the first or the second, in a rate book of 1803: 'Stroods and Mill – late Jeffrey, £17'. That was the amount at which it was assessed and evidently Jeffrey had given it up. Later in the century the mill was bought for £500. Nothing survives of either post mill.

The third Cuckfield mill was Whiteman's Green Smock Mill (TQ297253), also known as Beech Farm Mill. It was an unusually tall and narrow structure set among a complex of farm buildings that was bought at auction by Cuckfield Woodland Trust in May 1980. The smock was built in 1873 for the Sergison Estates to replace an earlier

The south side of the farm buildings complex: MLF 1983

mill a little to the north. The whole structure, including tail-fan, staging and a boat-shaped cap, was painted white. It had ceased working by 1918 and was dismantled four years later when the base was roofed. The last mention of this mill was on a one-inch 1922 Ordnance Survey tourist map of Brighton and the South Downs.

Earnley

Thought to be the last working windmill in Sussex to carry canvas sweeps, Earnley Mill (SZ817984), an octagonal smock on a stone and brick roundhouse, was first noted on the 1813 OS map and was still in use grinding barley meal for pigs and other stock as late as 1946, when it finally ceased working.

This smock was known as the Queen of West Sussex Windmills as the unusual shape, weatherboarded beehive cap, curious wooden gallery and two cloth-covered sweeps set it apart as a romantic landmark, according to Thurston Hopkins. In its original form the wooden tower stood low on the ground, but in later years it was jacked up on to a brick base to better reap the wind. An inscription

Earnley Mill, 'the Queen of West Susex windmills': C S Harding

in the brickwork reads 'F.B. 1827', which a 1920s miller believed was the date the mill was heightened and the gallery added. It is said a mill has stood on this spot for more than 300 years, but this is probably not it. Earnley Mill is more likely to have been built around the turn of the eighteenth and nineteenth centuries. The weather-boarded, black-tarred smock, also known as Somerley Mill, was bought in 1845 by the Stevens brothers and subsequently owned by that family for the following ninety-seven years.

Earnley Mill had two pairs of overdrift stones, one of which was composition. In 1870 a pair of peaks was added, these being driven first by a steam engine and then by an oil-engine.

The miller during the Second World War was a man called Ellis. He retired in 1942 and the mill was taken over by the Bartholomews of Chichester. It was allowed to deteriorate until acquired by Colin Darby in 1958. Mr Darby and his son Peter then began a long and extensive restoration.

The dismantled crown wheel and shaft: MLF 1983

The mill is in the grounds of a private residence on the road between Bracklesham and Birdham – and, regrettably, is in a very parlous state.

'Being rather small, this mill has a dainty look,' wrote Brunnarius. 'Earnley must be a lady, all be it slightly inebriated.'

The last windmill in Sussex to work with canvas sweeps, pictured in 1983: MLF

Felpham

Nothing remains of twin black and white mills beside the sea at Felpham. The earlier was Black Mill (SZ948994), first recorded on a map in 1760. Its sister, White Mill (SZ950994), was a few years younger.

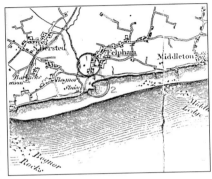

Detail from the OS map of 1813: MLF has circled the two sites

Towards the end of the nineteenth century newly-built houses 'robbed it (Black Mill) of its wind', it ceased to work and the sweeps were removed to reduce the rates on the property. The structure became unstable and was demolished in December 1902.

White Mill was worked until 1878 but encroachment on the site by the sea made it unusable and the mill was dismantled the following year. All trace has been lost now, although it was said that in the 1930s the foundations were visible occasionally at low tide.

Ferring

The famously eccentric John Olliver was once the miller of Highdown Old Mill (TQ085044), a very old structure marked on a survey of the coast of Sussex by Sir Thomas Palmer and Walter Covert in 1587. It was erected in the south-western corner of ancient earthworks on Highdown Hill, and ground corn for 236 years before being pulled down in 1826-27.

This long-gone post mill, of which very little is known and nothing remains, continues to be part of the folklore of the county for its very singular owner, Olliver, the miller of Lancing Down, who took on the old post mill on Highdown Hill in 1750. As well as working mills, Olliver – 'a stout, active cheerful man' – was believed to be heavily involved in the smuggling trade, and he could turn his hand to most things mechanical. Over his house he put up an automatic device that showed a smuggler being pursued by an excise officer who, in turn, was followed by an old woman with a broom. At the age of fifty-seven Olliver began to make preparations for his death. He had a wheeled coffin made – and stowed it beneath his bed (most likely laden with smuggled goods) – and built an ostentatiously grand hilltop tomb (TQ095042) ornamented with scriptural texts and poems of his own composition. Was brandy and French lace hidden here, too?

Twenty-seven years later, when Olliver eventually died aged eighty-four, two thousand mourners, and a number of young women dressed in white muslin, it is said, accompanied his coffin up the hill for his entombment. A girl of twelve read the service and

John Olliver's tomb on the summit of Highdown Hill

preached a sermon from Micah VII, verses 5-9.

In his will Olliver left an annuity of £20 a year to be spent on the upkeep of his tomb, and of the summerhouse he had built nearby and where he spent the very last years of his life as an anchorite. The tomb remains, the summerhouse does not.

When this old mill was taken down in 1826 a replacement was put up nearby and named Highdown New Mill. It had a relatively short career, its working life being over by 1880. According to Frederick

Luck, last owner of Angmering Post Mill, his father worked this mill and he declared that:

> Not one in ten thousand could tell you where that stands. It is the mystery mill of Sussex, and almost a local secret ... if you take the road by the Spotted Cow and find a footpath running up the hill by Ecclesden Manor, that will bring you to New Mill Cottages and the mill.

Long disused, the tower's shell was filled with bricks, and ivy was allowed to disguise its outer shape. The Ordnance Survey requested that the shell be allowed to remain as a landmark.

See also Highdown New Mill, page 14.

Findon

One mile north-east of Findon church a mill (TQ127091) was shown marked on maps between 1823 and 1875. Nothing remains.

Fishbourne

From medieval times Fishbourne was served by a number of watermills and it was not until one known as the Water Corn Mill was replaced by a galleried smock in the 1830s that the first windmill was built here. This was Barnet's Mill, which burned down in about 1866. Nothing is known of the second smock mill seen behind Barnett's Mill in Nibbs' drawing on the following page.

Feaver's Post Mill at Barnham, marked on maps from 1724 to 1823 was moved to Fishbourne in 1823.

Fishbourne Mill, a breast-shot watermill, could work only when the sluice gates were open at nearby Saltmill, whose owner, James Shepherd, was known to be a difficult man. As a result the sluice gates often remained closed. So the owner of Fishbourne, a man named Farne, bought an old open trestle post mill and had it set up beside his watermill.

The West Sussex Gazette and County Advertiser of October 29, 1857, reported:

From a drawing by R H Nibbs between 1860 and 1870 of Fishbourne harbour, showing two smock mills, one behind the other

A windmill was removed bodily from Rustington to Fishbourne a distance of upwards of 12 miles last week. It passed over Arundel bridge drawn by 9 horses with others in reserve, and it caused some wonder to see such a ponderous thing passing. It was laid on its side and reached even then nearly as high as the tops of some of the houses. The same windmill has been moved bodily before and, we believe, reached its destination safely.

The post mill (SU838044), known as Shepherd's Mill, fell into disuse around 1891 when an engine was installed in its companion watermill. It was pulled down in 1898 and ended its days as firewood.

The fallen post mill waiting to be chopped up for firewood

Henfield

There are no map references, no illustrations and no remains of an ancient windmill at the northern end of Henfield, yet one is known to have existed through tantalising references in a 1612 Will, a 1647 survey and a 1651 baptismal entry. The Will was that of Thomas Canon who:

> ... after bequests to other children, item, I give to Jane Canon my daughter my house wherein I now dwell together with the windmill and sixe acres of land more or less adjoyning (after the decease of Jane my wife) which house barns mill and land I give unto my wife during her life and after her decease to the said Jane my daughter and her heires for ever.

The survey by 'Commissioners appointed by Trustees of Parliament' was of the Manor at Henfield and refers to a windmill 'now in the tenure of John Gratwicke of Shermanbury' but does not mention a location.

Nep Town Mill

The baptismal reference came about because at that time and in that place the community shared just a handful of names. On October 3 1651, an entry was made of the baptism of Mary Hill 'daughter of Thomas (windmill) Hill and of Elizabeth Persis his wife'. The insertion of windmill is explained by the next

44

New Mill in 1910

entry, that of Jane Hill, daughter of Thomas Hill and of Persis his wife' on October 9.

But a Henfield windmill that *was* documented was Old Mill (TQ207156) at Nep Town (the upper section of the village also once known as Kneptowne and Uptowne). This was a post mill, first noted in 1724 and last seen on the Greenwood map of 1825. It was said that the mill, high on its hill, was marked by Trinity House as a landmark for those at sea. For this reason it could not be pulled down, even though in ruins. Eventually, though, a fierce gale in February 1908 tore apart the old mill's stout oak timbers and it fell.

Henfield New Mill (TQ217155) on Barrow Hill was a much younger post mill, built possibly when the 100-year-old Nep Town Mill fell into disuse. From a glass 'lookout' above the grain floor, shipping could be seen at sea through the Shoreham Gap. The so-called 'lantern' is accounted for by the then owner's interest in astronomy.

New Mill was worked until 1885 and then became disused. It was surveyed in 1935 by James Martin with a view to restoration. He

New Mill as it was at the time of James Martin's survey in August 1935

New Mill falls to the ground on October 21, 1953

found the mill to be supported on 'four brick piers each set high and constructed below ground level. The centre post is composed of four oak trees, squared and pegged together. It is 2ft 9in wide and 10ft 6in high and its edges are stop-chamfered.' The sweeps, Martin noted, were 'very rotten and only held together by innumerable coats of paint'. He concluded that the mill was in a fair state of repair and, if the weather boarding were replaced, could stand for many more years. But no further action was taken.

On Good Friday, April 7, 1950, a fire – although quickly extinguished – sealed New Mill's fate and in May 1953 the owner, C H White of Holedean Farm, advertised it for sale, to be demolished. No buyer came forward and it then went under the hammer at Steyning on October 17. Again, there was no buyer but the mill was sold by private treaty the following day to a Mr Hatcher of Brighton. Just three days later a lorry arrived at the site, a wire rope was attached to the mill and within half an hour it collapsed to the ground.

A steam mill was built near Henfield railway station towards the end of the nineteenth century to take on the task of grinding flour for the locality, but this too ceased working and was converted to 'a chemist's factory'. Nothing remains.

High Salvington

Salvington Mill (also known as Durrington Mill, and still standing today) was built around 1750 and is a black post mill set 320ft above sea level on Salvington Hill. At one time it was thought to have used a living oak tree, growing on the spot, as its post. Sadly, twentieth century restoration work disproved this pleasing fancy. The mill's shuttered sweeps are 58ft diameter x 7ft 6in wide. The crown tree bears the seal of the Sun Insurance Company, dated 1774.

This mill (TQ123067) was one of several that served the Worthing area in the eighteenth and nineteenth centuries. It was last worked in 1897, although it's believed the mill was brought back into use for a short time during the First World War. In fact a condition of the mill's sale after it became disused was that the machinery should be kept in such a state that work could start again immediately should the need arise.

Salvington Mill

By 1912 the timber roundhouse had been replaced by a tea room which remained until well into the 1950s. Mill enthusiast Peter Casebow remembered visiting the tea room as a child 'gazing at the large white sails, or sweeps as they are called in Sussex. Little did I realise then that I should become actively involved in its restoration nearly 30 years later.'

In 1959 Worthing Borough Council bought the mill and the Burgess Hill millwright Edwin Hole was engaged to replace some of the heavy structural timbers and attach new sweeps. The cost to the council was said to be £5,000. Then, during a gale in 1976, one of the huge stocks broke and fell to the ground and a subsequent survey revealed deathwatch beetle and a seriously weakened trestle.

*A 1920s Salmon postcard from a watercolour by A Quinton, showing the
tea room; the same Salmon postcard was later printed with the people painted out*

That same year a trust was set up to save Salvington Mill and a
dedicated nucleus of volunteers began what was to become years of
arduous, complex and back-breaking work to bring the mill back to
its original condition. They were from all walks of life and, as well as
Mr Casebow, were Felipe Edwards, Roger Ashton, Paul Royce, Ron
Hurd and John Pelling.

Horsham

A well-endowed community, Horsham was served by six windmills,
the earliest of which was Wimblehurst Mill (TQ177318), shown on
maps between 1724 and 1823-61. It was a post mill and was known to
have blown down. Another post mill, seen on maps between 1795
and 1825, was Compton Mill (TQ186317) of which nothing remains.
Champions Mill (TQ182314), first noted in 1813, was blown down
some time after its last reference in 1825. It stood close to the site of
the gallows on Horsham Common. Warnham Mill (TQ174321)

appears to be the shortest-lived of Horsham's windmills. It was built on a site opposite the Dog and Bacon Inn and was seen only on the 1823-24 and 1825 maps. Star Mill was located east of the road (TQ191316) on the 1813 OS map, and west of the road (TQ189316) on the 1826 Greenwood map. It had, however, been noted since 1796 and the Greenwood reference was its last. The mill was pulled down.

Much better known was Cripplegate Mill (TQ161254), a tall black smock dating from the early eighteenth century. Its origins are vague, although

Cripplegate Mill

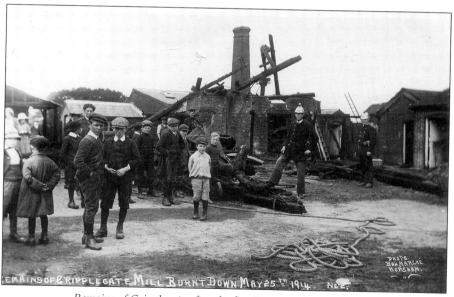

Remains of Cripplegate after the fire: Bon Marché, Horsham

reputedly the mill was moved to the town's Southwater area from Rusper – and further, that it had originated in Cripplegate, London, hence the name. It stood close to the site of the gallows on Horsham Common.

In the early hours of May 25, 1914, fire broke out in the mill. Horsham Fire Brigade was quickly on the scene but its fire-fighters were unable to save the mill, which was destroyed. The roundhouse remained for some years. See also under Rusper, page 70.

Hunston

A handsome smock, Hunston Mill (SU858009) on the Selsey Peninsula, also known as 'the windmill at Kipson Bank', was built in 1801 and was worked until about 1915. This was a large, ten-sided mill with a beehive cap and shuttered sweeps. A notice in *The Sussex Advertiser* of March 12, 1832, offered:

> ... particulars of an excellent freehold smock windmill in full trade, to be sold by Henry Salter at the Anchor Inn Chichester, Tuesday 20th March 1832. The mill is worked by two pairs of French stones and all tackle and fabric in good repair. The exterior of which has been newly canvassed and pitched.

The most prominent family of millers was the Hodsons. James Hodson bought the mill at auction in 1856 and when he died, aged seventy, in 1870, his son Charles took over. The Hodsons refitted the mill to work two pairs of peak stones and one of French burrs.

Charles Hodson took every opportunity to bedeck his mill with celebratory flags – like, for instance, the occasion of the opening of the Selsey Tramway on August 27, 1897, when Hunston Mill was dressed overall, as it was for Empire Day on May 24 every year.

The mill closed in 1915 and was pulled down in 1919. Only the roundhouse remains, roofed over and converted to a summer house.

Hunston Mill flag-bedecked on August 27, 1912, to celebrate the fifteenth anniversary of the Selsey Tramway

Ifield

The Old Mill (TQ251379) at Ifield, not marked on any maps, was moved to its site a quarter of a mile north-east of the parish church from Bletchingley in about 1870, according to H E S Simmons, author of the *Sussex Windmill Survey*. A post mill, it was demolished in 1899, leaving only the roundhouse standing.

In August 1960 Crawley Nautical Training Corps, TS Courageous, took over the roundhouse for use as a new headquarters. A report in *The Evening News* of August 29, 1960, stated:

> It was there that in 1860 the first steam engine in the country to be used for the grinding of grain was installed. In 1926 it was removed to the Science Museum, London.

Nothing remains at the site now, but some of the trestle timbers can be seen in Goff's Park, Crawley (TQ 260363).

Jolesfield

Built around 1788, the smock mill at Jolesfield Common (TQ191205) was known at various times throughout its long life as West Grinstead Mill, Jolesfield or Joulsfield Mill, Partridge Green Mill and Littleworth Mill. Thurston Hopkins had this to say about it:

At night there is a poignant melancholy about the Jolesfield Mill ... standing against the crimson sunset-flushes, with its great sweeps cutting the sky into sections, it makes up the authentic chiaroscuro of elf-land.

Jolesfield's girth was larger than that of the usual smock and it had an unusual beehive design cap with a large penthouse doorway giving access to the fanstage. The tower was capacious enough to take four pairs of underdrift stones, two pairs of peaks and two pairs of burrs.

Business at the mill was badly hit when a steam mill opened at Partridge Green in 1914, and it was last worked in 1928. Then followed many years of dereliction and decay until in 1959, the owner, Nevvar Hicmet, decided to

Jolesfield Mill: Frith postcard

move the mill to his Gatwick Manor Hotel and Restaurant and restore it as a working attraction – also to supply power to the hotel. Jolesfield was in a sadly dilapidated state externally, with disintegrating sweeps, yet the inside was said to be as sound as a bell.

Millwright Edwin Hole was called in to dismantle the windmill – against the protests of locals, who did not want their mill taken away. The machinery was moved and the body dismantled, with its parts being numbered for reassembly. But re-erection at the new site proved impractical for a number of reasons and the plan was abandoned. The brick base was converted into a stable and the huge timber and iron machinery decayed. Meanwhile, at Gatwick Manor, a mock windmill was erected and the Jolesfield parts that had already been carted to the site were allowed to rot.

In recent years those pieces which were salvageable have been removed and put on display at Lowfield Heath Windmill (TQ234407).

They move a windmill

IT'S GOING FROM PARTRIDGE GREEN TO GATWICK

THE famous old Jolesfield windmill near Partridge Green, Sussex, is now being pulled down—but it will rise again on a new site in Surrey. Dismantling work con-

restored to full working order in the grounds of the 13th-century Gatwick Manor, on the London to Brighton road. Mr. Edwin Hole (seen at a window in the picture above), who is one of Britain's few surviving millwrights, is in charge of the dismantling. The framework of the mill is being sawn through and each of the octagonal sides will be transported complete by road. It is expected that the mill will be working again by

Report in the News Chronicle, August 19, 1959: millwright Edwin Hole, in charge of dismantling, is seen at the window

54

Keymer

Oldland Mill (standing and restored) was mentioned in a 1755 Ditchling churchwarden's account and first noted on a map in 1703. The origins, however, are obscure. Is this the same mill as that mentioned in the church records?

A post mill, set on Lodge Hill (TQ321163), it is a white-painted structure on a brick roundhouse. Originally it was an open-trestle mill, but then the lower part was covered in for storage purposes – not with a roundhouse, as was traditional, but with an octagonal house. The mill worked two pairs of stones.

David Driver was the last miller to work Oldland by wind. At the outbreak of World War One he left to become a corn merchant in Hassocks. By now the mill was idle and over time it deteriorated until the last private owner, a Mr Turner, handed it over to Sussex Archaeological Trust in 1927.

In July 1934 the *Sussex County Magazine* reported that 'an SOS had been sent out to all lovers of picturesque Sussex to help in

Oldland Mill in 1910: Kingsway postcard

55

Patched up and propped up:
drawing, Fred Ingrams

saving Oldland Mill, which is threatened with dissolution'. The Trust had intended to have the windmill restored and preserved as an example of the many king-post mills once so plentiful in the county. A small agricultural museum in the roundhouse, open to the public at sixpence a head, was the only revenue available to the restoration fund.

But continuous gales played havoc with the structure and eventually it was no longer safe to admit the public and the mill's only income was cut off. 'If the public wish to save this well-known landmark and at the same time preserve a vestige of older Sussex, they must come to the rescue,' the *SCM* stated. A 'shilling fund' was opened to raise the estimated £150 needed and readers were asked to send a shilling postal order to Arthur Hill, treasurer of Oldland Mill Preservation Fund. 'Another gale and it may be too late,' they were warned. The public sent Mr Hill just £12. Thundered the SCM:

> What, one wonders, is the position of the Sussex Archaeological Trust in relation to its guardianship of Oldland Mill? A nominal one, for in the day of trouble it is found that the Trust is not in a position to act as guardian!

The mill continued to stand, albeit deteriorating more and more as the years went by, until in 1980 Hassocks, Keymer, Clayton and Ditchling villages joined forces to prevent a catastrophic collapse. A village amenity society succeeded in leasing the mill from the Trust at a peppercorn rent. The new carers, appealing for cash help, described the mill as: 'A very senior citizen, badly in need of an old age pension, supplementary benefit and a debility allowance.'

The mill was patched up and propped up and another campaign

was launched to raise £30,000. The newspaper report from *The Daily Telegraph* of October 3, 1995, right, tells of the fourteen years a group of enthusiasts had already spent on restoration and the projected further ten years until Oldland Mill was once again in perfect working order.

Mill restorers face 25 years of hard grind

From the Daily Telegraph, October 3, 1995

The first piece of rotting timber was removed in 1981. 'We all still had jobs – three of us engineers and the others a teacher, a sales executive, a printer and an architect,' said John Arnett, a retired engineer. 'We are all retired, and we estimate we still have more than ten years to go before the sweeps are turning again.'

The sweeps were removed in 1981; the trestle rebuilt in 1987; the crown tree replaced in 1988; new frames built for the body in 1991-93; the old mill body was dismantled in 1995; it was re-erected in 1996-98; new cladding was added in 2001-03; and the roundhouse was reconstructed in 2004. A grant was awarded by DEFRA to replace the sweeps and the brake wheel, for overhauling the tail wheel, re-dressing the millstones, replacing the skirt above the roundhouse and re-laying the brick floor of the roundhouse.

Money to make Oldland a working mill again was, and is still being raised by local coffee mornings and sales, and by occasional small grants. The Mill is open by appointment and on certain Sundays and Thursdays; call 01273 503747.

Kirdford

Kirdford had a windmill about which nothing is known except that in 1800 it was moved to Coolham.

L

Lancing

Lancing Mill pictured in 1890

There were, at one time, three windmills at Lancing, two early post mills from the eighteenth century and a later post type known as Lancing Mill (TQ184062), which was marked on maps between 1813 and 1874. Apparently there was enough wind for only one mill in the locality and the decision was made for the two older ones to be taken down. Lancing Mill was known to be working in 1895 and was pulled down in 1905.

Thurston Hopkins, in *Old Watermills and Windmills,* wrote:

Lancing Down Mill has gone the way of all good mills and resolutions, and nothing now remains to tell of its whereabouts. Seemingly it stood near the chalk pits at the meeting place of tracks running to Coombes and Leechpool.

Littlehampton

A port town serving a rich corn-growing area, Littlehampton was once known as The Little Holland of Sussex for the number of its windmills. Perhaps the earliest was a post mill, Cudlow Mill (TQ033015), noted on maps only between 1813 and 1824, although it was probably much older and certainly it stood for much longer than the latter date suggests. It was also called Littlehampton Mill and was sited close to the beach, a little south-east of the church. The picture, right, shows a small mill beside the Beach Coffee House in 1795. Although this appears to bear little

The Beach Coffee House c1795

resemblance to the picture of Cudlow Mill from an old drawing (below), which described the mill as 'about 200 years old' – it may well be the same building, or a precedessor on the same site.

Arun Mill, a fine four-floor tower mill, was the subject of innumerable picture postcards, and was painted by Constable. The sweeps powered two pairs of French burr stones and one pair of Derby peak stones. A notable feature of this mill is that when a replacement shaft was needed, the mast of the Duke of Norfolk's yacht *Arundel* was used. The *Arundel* was one of the famous racing yachts of the 1850s and used to lie in a small dock in Pier Road.

Cudlow Mill – on the beach

Arun Mill was a well-known local landmark, built in 1831 by millwright Henry Martin of Bognor. A year later Martin sold the mill for £726 to William Halsted Boniface, 'yeoman of Yapton, miller and mealman' who, in 1836, granted a twenty-one-year lease to Robert Carter of Lewes. Four years after this the lease was transferred to John Woodhams, in whose family the mill remained for the next seventy years. Woodhams dealt in agricultural seeds, clovers, grass, Italian rye grass, turnips, trifolium and tares, and many foreign vessels entered the port with cargoes of cereals and oil cake for his firm. Boniface, still the owner, died in 1849 and the mill, which was heavily mortgaged, went to the mortgagee Charles Newman, of Patcham. Woodhams, leaseholder of the mill, and John Burtenshaw, tenant of one of the cottages, thereafter paid their rent to Newman. After Newman's death the mill, bakehouse, brew-house, stable, coach house, piggeries and two cottages were put up for sale and in May 1854 were bought by Thomas Crunden of Brighton for £1,080. Then, the lease granted to Robert Carter expired and Woodhams bought the property from Crunden for £1,075.

It was said that from the top of Arun Mill fifteen other mills could be seen. These were at Rustington, Lyminster, Clymping, Barnham, Arundel, Felpham, Angmering, Walberton, Slindon, Boxgrove and Salvington. Sometimes, if weather conditions were right, the mill at Selsey Bill could also be seen.

John Woodham and Sons worked the mill until 1901 after which a series of millers took it on for a year or so each. Finally, in 1913 the mill became derelict, although it remained very much a feature in the townscape. The tower was unaffected by the stiff sea winds, but over

Arun Mill in 1906: Valentine's postcard

A Valentine's postcard of 1917 shows the landmark mill beyond the fashionable promenade

the years the cap fell in and the sweeps were stripped of their shutters.

The ninety-nine year lease on the land, owned by the Duke of Norfolk, expired in 1930 and although a brave fight was put up by conservationists to restore and preserve the mill as an asset to the town, perhaps 'surrounded with pleasant grounds where good Sussex teas might be served from thatched pavilions', it was to no avail. The mill was demolished in 1932 and the site replaced with Butlin's amusement park.

Sad state of Arun Mill in 1930

The Canon postcard, left, of Lowfield Heath Mill, was posted in 1907; above the mill in 1971: MLF

Lowfield Heath

The post mill here (TQ270398), a landmark on the Brighton to London road since coaching days, was erected in the 1760s just to the west of what was to become the A23 – there were claims it was moved to Lowfield Heath from Hookwood (although no record exists of a mill being at Hookwood until 1820) – and it was last in use in about 1880. Originally a Surrey windmill, Lowfield Heath became a Sussex mill when the county boundaries were revised in 1974.

A feature of the mill, which stood on a two-storey tarred brick roundhouse, and had only two floors, was the way the body was extended well back from the crown tree. Although all post mills were built like this to counterbalance the sweep assembly, it was exaggerated in the case of Lowfield Heath, with only one-third of the body in front of the post. Brunnarius commented that 'this certainly prevented her becoming head-sick, a common failing in an old post-mill'.

After it ceased working in 1880 the mill deteriorated and the big storm of August 1958 tore away its last two sweeps and part of the roof. Over the years that followed it began to crumble and faced the prospect of being swamped by the ever-encroaching Gatwick Airport complex since it stood just a few hundred yards south of the runway. Vandalised and decaying, the mill was taken on by Surrey County Council and The Society for the Protection of Ancient Buildings in the late 1960s, and millwright Edwin Hole was employed to make good the structure.

In the 1980s enthusiasts came up with a scheme to save the mill, one of only forty-seven post mills surviving in the country. A total of more than £100,000 had to be raised to restore the mill, and to move it to a new home at Charlwood Zoo and Aviaries. The mill was dismantled during the summer of 1987, moved, rebuilt (TQ234407) and put back into working order by Lowfield Heath Windmill Trust, which now cares for the mill. It is open to the public on National Mills Day and the last Sunday of each month from May to the end of August, 2-5pm, or by appointment. Entry is by donation.

Lyminster

Were there one, two or three mills at Lyminster? Maurice Lawson Finch's research reveals one, Brookfield Mill (TQ028054) marked on maps between 1753 and 1824; a second, Toddington Mill (TQ029042), seen on maps of 1812 and 1823 only; and a third which, confusingly, was revealed as 'Toddington Mill, formerly Brookfield Mill'. This last (TQ029042) was marked on only the 1875 map. It seems possible that Brookfield, which was moved from its original site north-east of the church to Mill Lane, south-east of the church, was renamed Toddington Mill from its new locality at Tortington, and that there was no third mill. All that remains as a reminder of a windmill at Lyminster is the neighbourhood name Millhouse.

From the 1813 OS map, marked by MLF

Newtimber

An early windmill is known to have existed at Newtimber, half a mile or so east-north-east of the church. It was marked on maps of 1724 and 1763, but nothing now remains to show its whereabouts.

North Mundham

A windmill called Runcton, about which nothing is known, was once here.

North Stoke

Campfield Mill was here in the eighteenth century, marked only on the 1780 map. Nothing remains. Stoke Mill (TQ029122) may have been its replacement. This was seen on maps of 1823 and 1824. Again, nothing remains.

Nutbourne

The barn to the south of Nutbourne is generally accounted the largest in Sussex, and, according to *Hidden Sussex* of 1984, ... 'next to it is a round house, octagonal with a superb kingpost roof. Wave this book and the farmer will make you welcome.' Alas, the waving of the book no longer applies. Maurice wondered if the 'round house' was the remnant of the elusive Nutbourne Mill on the Hampshire border. On a visit to the village in 1997 he had a long discussion with two local residents, both of whom told him 'there had never been a windmill at

Nutbourne – but there had been one a mile and a half towards Emsworth at Southbourne.

Maurice maintained that there was in fact a mill within the hamlet, basing this on a history of the district by Arthur Mee which mentioned two mills in Nutbourne, 'one of which was standing as late as 1846'. Did the round house remains belong to this mill?

The other was the well-documented Nutbourne Tower Mill, which had immensely thick walls of stone and brick. The sandstone and yellow brick tower was heavily tarred and the windmill worked two pairs of underdrift stones, one peak, one burr, that were driven by patent sweeps. Its working days ceased around the turn of the nineteenth and twentieth centuries, when it was left to become derelict.

Nutbourne Mill, its sweeps laid on top:
drawing, Chris Wilkins 1976

More recently Brunnarius stated there were three mills at Nutbourne in the 1880s. The tower mill built in the 1850s (TQ078189) and two watermills. All three were operated together, with a bakery business. The windmill worked for only about forty years before the fan was blown off in 1894. In 1908 it became part of a holiday retreat for the children of Dr Barnardo's Homes, although the windmill itself could not have been used for residential purposes as most of the machinery remained in the tower for many decades.

In the mid-1930s the windmill was surveyed by the Reverend Peter Hemming who noted that it was 'in a sorry state of repair'.

Doors, windows and galleries had all disappeared and only the middlings of the four sweeps – along with the windshaft and part of the fan tackle – remained in position.

Oving

Just one old map, the 1813 first edition of the one-inch Ordnance Survey, shows a mill at Oving (SU905049). Seven years later only the site could be seen on the 1920 edition of the same map.

The 1813 OS map

Pagham

'Holiday crowd sees mill blaze' was the *Evening Argus* headline of June 15, 1962. 'Children are thought to have started a fire and badly damaged 200-year-old Pagham Mill,' said the report. 'As flames leapt through the mill's copper roof villagers and holidaymakers watched Bognor Regis firemen battling to save the historic building. Among onlookers was 70-year-old John Durman, the last miller. He said: "I'm sure this was started by boys. They have been breaking in regularly for the past year." Firemen were hampered by the threat of 5.5 tons of millstones on the second

Nyetimber Mill before the sweeps and fan were removed in 1926

floor crashing down on them. They fought the flames for three hours and managed to save the mill, which belongs to Mr. Baker Beale, of Mill Farm, Pagham, from being completely destroyed.'

The mill had ceased working in 1915 because of the government's wartime ban on the grinding of grain for cattle and poultry foods. Also, the mill had been tail-winded, and the machinery damaged.

This was Nyetimber tower mill (SZ892988), described by the *Argus* as 200 years old. The mill was not marked on any map until 1900, although dates ranging from 1762 to 1840 have been given for its erection. Maurice listed it as having been built in the 1840s for William Adams, who was still in occupation in 1887.

The copper-covered ogee cap had a fringed wooden petticoat to keep out the rain and the four-storey tower carried a high-mounted fan and gallery. Patent sweeps drove two pairs of French burrs and a flour dresser. In the mill's later years a converted railway

A derelict hulk is the backdrop of a caravan park in 1953

engine was installed in a shed to provide auxiliary steam power.

The machinery was damaged after becoming 'tail-winded' and the mill fell into disuse. The sweeps were crippled by a storm in 1926 and removed in 1927. For a period the Durman family leased the mill, using the ground floor as a carpenter's shop, but it was empty from the mid-1930s and what remained of the windmill was left to become derelict. The immediate surroundings changed from picturesque cottages and meadows to a bleak caravan camping field in the 1950s.

Perhaps the young arsonists did the mill a favour by forcing a restoration – although Maurice considered the result 'sterile'.

In the 1980s the body was refurbished, given a gleaming silver cap and became the focal point of a little estate of retirement homes.

A new role for Nyetimber: MLF 1983

Another windmill that *was* 200 years old was Pagham Mill (SZ885967), marked on maps from 1788 but mentioned much earlier in a survey of 1736. It was built at Pagham Point, near a watermill pond, by Thomas Peckwell. Nothing remains.

Parham

A map of 1719 showed a windmill here a quarter of a mile north-east of the church. Nothing remains.

Petworth

A mill at Petworth (SU978215) was marked on maps between 1823 and 1825. No evidence remains.

Plaistow

Pullen's Mill, seen on only the 1823-24 map, was pulled down.

Pulborough

A locality well-endowed with windmills, Pulborough had three, the earliest being North Heath Old Mill, shown on a map of 1795 to be two miles north-east of Pulborough church, and now gone. It was perhaps replaced by Heath Mill (TQ061208), half a mile away and noted on maps from 1813 to 1825. Nothing remains today.

Pulborough Mill (TQ058185), seen on the same maps, was three-quarters of a mile east-south-east from the church and was known to have blown down.

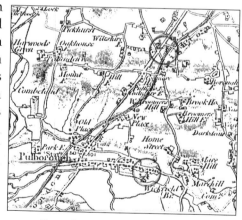

From the 1813 OS map; MLF has circled the positions of two of the mills

Rudgwick

Here there were three mills, all now vanished. Rudgwick Mill (TQ082346), half a mile north-west of the parish church, was known to exist between 1800 and 1823. Possibly older were Rowhook Honeylane Mill (TQ122351), marked on maps from 1795 to 1823, and sited two miles east of the church, and Rowhook Mill (TQ122346) for which there are no map references.

Rusper

Rusper Mill was built c1792 by James Ridge, a Horsham millwright, and first appeared on a map of 1795. It was a smock mill with patent sweeps winded by a fantail that drove two pairs of stones and a dressing machine. The mill was burned down in March 1894.

Rustington

Bridge Mill (TQ055029), or Humphrey's Mill after the family who worked it for much of the nineteenth century, was built in the middle of the eighteenth century and succeeded an even earlier mill mentioned in records of 1660-61 on the same site, which was half a mile north-north-east of the church. Bridge Mill – a post mill – ceased working around the turn of the nineteenth and twentieth centuries and was pulled down in 1913. There were several mill movements in the Arundel, Angmering, Rustington and Fishbourne area in the eighteenth and nineteenth centuries and it was once thought that Bridge Mill came from Angmering, where it could have been Jerusalem Mill, which disappeared from maps in 1823.

A rare sight – a scan of a photocopy of the only known photograph of Bridge Mill

However, research by Mary Taylor of Rustington in the 1970s and 1980s makes this unlikely. Mrs Taylor traced references to Bridge Mill being in Rustington from 1763 when a 'Mr Nolson of Bridge Mill' paid £10 poor relief.

Nor could this be the post mill that was moved to Fishbourne in 1857 since, in 1895, it was advertised to let in the *West Sussex Gazette* as 'a good windmill, with stable, coach house, piggeries and cottage if desired at Rustington, half a mile from Angmering station'.

Rustington Mill, also known as Sea Mill and Seafield Mill, was another post mill seen on maps between 1823 and 1909. It was built close to the sea in about 1805 (an advertisement in the *Littlehampton News* of June 1889 declaring it to have been established 'nearly 100 years') and was described in *Watermills and Windmills, A History of Corn Milling* (1898) as 'the latest

The 1981 sign outside The Windmill Inn at Rustington; the north face, above, shows a post mill while the south face shows a smock mill: MLF

71

Seafield Mill: M T Mason

form of the turret mill'. In 1812 a Mr Graves became the miller and his family then owned the mill until about 1874.

In 1903, while the mill still stood, but was no longer in use, the site was acquired by The Metropolitan Asylums Board for a children's convalescent home, which was built in 1906. In 1912 a fierce storm and encroaching waves from the sea caused serious damage to the mill and undermined its base. It was pulled down in 1913.

There were other mills at Rustington of which nothing remains, and information is scant. As well as the so-called Early Mill that

A turn of the century scene – notice the curious vehicle on the left; a horse bus?

72

After the storm of 1912

may have been Bridge Mill's predecessor, there was an 'unknown' mill a short distance south-east of Early Mill and Bridge Mill, and another 'unknown' mill close to the Seafield Mill. This seems likely to have been the post mill that was moved from Rustington to Fishbourne in 1857. See Fishbourne, page 43.

Selham

Maps between 1795 and 1825 show that a mill existed (SU927216) at Moorland Farm a little north of Selham. Nothing remains.

Selsey

A tourist attraction of the Selsey peninsula is Medmerry Mill (SZ844 934), a handsome red-brick tower dating from the nineteenth century and standing just yards from the shingle scarp.

Contrast the rural scene of Medmerry Mill in the Photocrom postcard above with that of the post-Second World War holiday camp seen on the opposite page

Above, the holiday camp, right, Medmerry in 1969

Last of a succession of mills on the Medmerry marshes, the present tower was built in about 1820, and its white beehive cap was surrounded by a gallery – the only example of its kind in Sussex – to enable the miller to furl and unfurl the canvas-rigged sweeps. The mill had two pairs of stones, one peak, one burr.

After the last flour was milled at Selsey in the early 1890s, the mill stood idle for a short period and then was comprehensively updated in 1907-08 with new windshaft, four patent sails, a rebuilt cap, gallery and fan. The old machinery was replaced with modern equipment for cracking beans and rolling oats. But because of restrictive conditions during the First World War, business fell away and the mill ended its working days grinding pepper.

In its original setting of farm buildings and trees Medmerry Mill was described by G M Fowell in 1920 as 'a precious feature in a somewhat uninteresting landscape'. What a contrast by 1959 when a holiday camp was set up by the White Horse Caravan Company in the shadow of the mill. The mill became part of the complex and housed a gift shop in its base, but camp owner John Bunn, a local man, also aimed to restore the mill which was still used as a landmark by seafarers using the Channel.

An ambitious programme began in 1960 and was completed a year later. Windows were glazed, dummy sweeps fitted as well as a new cap, and a large observation window was inserted on the seaward side.

The Windmill, Selsfield Common, Sussex.

Selsfield Common

The pretty smock here, Selsfield Common Mill (TQ344349), was built early in the nineteenth century – and first shown on the map of 1817. It worked for about a century, until 1894, and was demolished by 1909.

Shipley

There were three mills here, Smart's Mill, of which nothing is now known; Honeypoles Mill (TQ145212), a post mill that stood in a field near The Blacksmith's Arms, shown on maps between 1823 and 1876

A 1905 Homewood postcard of Shipley Mill

and known to have been pulled down; and the famous Shipley Mill (TQ143218). This, also known as Vincent's (from a one-time miller), Marten's or King's Mill, was the picturesque smock owned by writer and MP Hilaire Belloc. It was built in 1879 by Horsham millwrights

Ruinous state of Shipley in 1955

with the appropriate names of Grist and Steele, who, it's said, incorporated the shafts and machinery from an old mill at Coldwaltham. The mill stands on a two-storey octagonal base.

Shipley is the youngest of the Sussex smock mills, and the largest. The estimated cost of building the mill was £800, but actually it cost more than three times that at £2,500, which caused serious concern to the owner, Frend Marten.

Shipley carries four spring patent sweeps capable of driving three pairs of stones.

When Marten died his widow Sarah

Shipley: Chris Wilkins 1976

continued to run Shipley with a miller named Wood, then sold it in 1895 to Richard Vincent, who in turn sold it to Belloc in 1906 along with the adjacent house, King's Land. Belloc, born in France, spent much of his childhood in Slindon. He loved both his adopted county – and windmills, which were a primary reason for buying King's Land. J B Morton wrote of his friend that invariably when he returned from his walks, Belloc doffed his hat to 'Mrs Shipley' before entering his house.

An octagonal, galleried, five-storey structure, Shipley Mill was worked until 1926 by Ernest Powell, who was on a yearly tenancy. Then the sweeps were braked. It was said that Belloc (who was 'charmed by the rhythmic sough-clatter-and-rumble of the working mill and wrote many of his essays and poems to its music') objected to the noise of motor transport plying to and from the mill and interrupting his work.

Powell's son, Peter, recalled:

> On one occasion, when I was about seven, I was at Kingsland when Mr. Winston Churchill and Mr. G. K. Chesterton were visiting Mr. Belloc. They were often visitors and on this occasion they were playing cards and asked me to play, and what game would I like. I replied 'Jack-Out-o'Doors,' and there was I, a lad of seven, playing cards with these great men.

Belloc died in 1953.

In 1954 West Sussex County Council asked experts to prepare a report on the county's windmills. Shipley appeared to be the only one in a reasonable state of repair. At about the same time it was suggested it be restored as a memorial to Belloc and a committee was set up with Belloc's son-in-law Reginald Jebb as chairman and Peter Powell as treasurer. The county council offered to help on condition a sufficient sum was raised by private subscriptions. Donations came from home and abroad and £800 was raised by 191 contributors. Another £300 came from the Pilgrim Trust.

In an evocative report in *The Evening News* of Wednesday, March 19, 1958, Richard Herd wrote:

Fully restored, the smock in 1999: B W Finch

The millwright gazed up at the massive 70ft-high sails [in fact they are 98ft] – or sweeps as they call them locally – of Shipley's mill, slipped another shutter into position and in a proud Sussex burr told me: 'Give us a fair old breeze and that little old tail-fan'll catch it and swing those sweeps head-on into the wind.'

And when it does the great white sails will sweep round, the granite millstones will rumble and devour the maize, wheat and rye and grind them into flour for the first time for nigh on 30 years.

It's with justifiable pride that the millwright, 52-year-old Edwin Hole, of Burgess Hill, talks. It's taken him two years to bring the mill back to working order. And it's done with just as much pride that Sussex folk will on the appointed day stand beneath it and watch the flour cascade into the sacks. For they have contributed £800 towards the total cost of about £4,000.

Shipley Mill, regularly and lovingly maintained since that major rebuild, is open on National Mills Day and the first, second and third Sunday of each month from April to October, also bank holidays. Entry is by admission charge. Parties by appointment: call 01403 730439.

See page 9 for the sectional drawing of the interior made by James E Martin in 1925 showing the arrangement of Shipley's five floors.

Shoreham

There is documentary evidence of six windmills in this old harbour town, the earliest dating from 1230. This was mentioned in a 'fine' dated St Andrew's Day, Lewes, of that year, in which Henry III granted Thomas Scot and his wife Cicely an acre of land 'being that acre where the windmill is situated, together with the windmill and its appurtenances'.

Little information is available for the second oldest, except that it was shown in an engraving of Shoreham in 1645 by Wenceslaus Hollar. Then there were Old Mill in Mill Lane, seen on the 1813 OS map and, presumably its successor, New Mill – a tall black tower – on the same site, marked on maps of 1873 and 1909.

From a watercolour of Shoreham in 1899; Old Mill, Mill Lane or Old Black Mill?

A 1907 *Homelands Handbook*, Volume 59, had this:

> ... on the right (of Mill Lane) is a derelict windmill which, if it had sails, would knock down the houses that are clustered around it. Some old prints of the beginning of the last century show it working and an old coaching-way book says it was erected in 1764.

On Mill Hill were Ashby's Mill and another Old Mill, both marked on maps between 1724 and 1753 (could they have been the same mill?) – and also on the same hill was Old Black Mill (TQ212066), a post mill built c1764, that was burned down in 1899. This one was marked on maps between 1780 and 1873. It was also known as Good Friday Mill as Mill Hill was called Good Friday Hill. This came from the old Shoreham custom of rolling dyed, hard-boiled eggs and oranges down the steep side of the hill on Good Friday.

Slaugham

No evidence exists now of Cook's Mill on Mill Hill, nor does it of the locality's second windmill, Handcross or Worsfold's Mill, for which there is no map reference or site.

Slindon

Maps between 1719 and 1795 show a post mill here that local legend says was moved to Avisford Hill, Walberton, although no evidence of the move exists.

Sompting

Here, there were two mills, Upper Cokeham at Millfield, which is not marked on any maps and whose site has not been located – and a pumping mill seen on maps of 1901-03 and sited around a third of a mile south-south-west of Sompting church.

Southbourne

Gosden Green Mill's only references are on maps of 1778 and 1810. See Nutbourne on page 64.

South Harting

Nothing remains of Harting Hill Mill, seen on maps between 1724 and 1779, nor is anything now known about it other than that it was located about half a mile south-east of South Harting church.

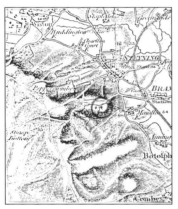

Steyning

Two eighteenth century windmills, Old Mill and Lashmar's Mill served the Steyning area before Steyning Mill (TQ175104), seen on maps from 1813 to 1875, was built on high ground between Steyning and Bramber. It was pulled down and nothing now remains.

Site of Steyning Mill, 1813 OS

Storrington

Black Mill (TQ082141) was a tarred post mill with brick roundhouse and cloth sweeps that stood in Kithurst Lane. It was marked on maps in 1780 and 1824, yet remained for a century or so after the last date. It was the last working mill in Storrington, having been completely overhauled in 1906; it ceased working in 1919 and was demolished in 1923. A residence called Cherry House was built on the site with one of the millstones being used for the front step. An earlier post mill, Bottings Mill, stood a short distance up the Chiltington road and worked in conjunction with a watermill nearby. It was destroyed by fire in 1868.

A Corder postcard of Storrington's Black Mill

Sullington

According to Mark Antony Lower's *History of Sussex*, there was a windmill here in the thirteenth century. It was part of the estate of Roger de Covert who owned a manor house (valued at three shillings

Another Corder postcard, this one showing 'Storrington's White Mill', which was actually on Sullington Warren

and fourpence), a park, two watermills and one windmill.

A post mill, Sullington Common Mill (TQ097143), was noted on maps between 1813 and 1900 and was sited on Sullington Warren. Also known as Warren Mill and Crowhurst's Mill, this white mill was an open-trestle design with common sweeps that worked two pairs of stones via a spur-gear drive taken from the brake wheel.

It was built around 1800 and ceased working in 1907 when the machinery was taken away for use in a nearby watermill operated by the same family (the Crowhursts). By this time the mill was close to collapse and an appeal was launched to make it safe and preserve it as a landscape feature for future generations. But it was not to be. Joan Ham in her book *Storrington in Pictures* wrote:

> The summer of 1911 was hot and dry. The gorse and bracken on The Warren caught fire and spread rapidly despite the

The same mill marked on this postcard as Sullington Mill.

Villagers gather to watch the last stand of Sullington Common Mill

efforts of many beaters. The horse-drawn fire engine summoned by telephone from Steyning galloped over at top speed but it was too late to save the mill.

The date was August 9.

The site of the old mill is marked by the cast iron windshaft mounted on concrete plinths. The mill was one of only two of this design to be found in Sussex. The other was at Clymping. The shaft has two cast cannisters, one for the compass arm brake wheel and the other for the two stocks on which the four sweeps were mounted.

Twineham

There are the remains here of a watermill that once had a windmill with sweeps winded by a large fan mounted on a skeletal framework – Hooker's Windmill and Watermill (TQ258203) – on its roof, similar to the combination mill at West Ashling. The watermill was built in 1851 for George Packham who had added the windmill in 1865 for one of his daughters – a Mrs Wood. It was marked on only the map of 1876. Four patent sweeps drove the upright shaft of the watermill through the hollow iron post of the trestle.

An advertisement in the *Miller* of February 7, 1876, reads:

> To let Hookers flour mill containing 5 pairs of stones, wind, steam and water. Situated 4 miles from Burgess Hill. Good mill house, smiths shop, bakehouse etc. Apply Mr. Wood, Hickstead.

The mill was let to a Mr C Packham of Cobbs Mill in 1886 when working by water ceased. The windmill was damaged in 1887 after which the stones were run by steam power for five years or so. Ernest Hole of Burgess Hill was employed to dismantle the mill machinery in 1900 and the remaining buildings were used for storage until they either fell down or were taken down.

Up Marden

No trace remains of Haslett Mill seen on the map of 1898 about a mile south-west of the church.

There is evidence of a second mill at Up Marden, Apple Down Mill (SU794152), seen on maps between 1813 and 1829. It was a cloth-sailed post mill which operated two pairs of French burrs. It was destroyed by fire in March, 1844.

*Apple Down Mill circled
by MLF on the 1813
OS map*

Walberton

Avisford Mill (SU971072), set on the Slindon-Walberton boundary, was said to have been taken here from Slindon (whose own windmill was not seen on maps after 1795; Avisford was first noted in 1813). There is no documentary evidence for the move, only local legend.

The last miller was William Luxford, who took over at a time of falling trade, and with the windmill needing repairs that the landlord refused to pay for, and wanted demolished. The unfortunate William also had asthma, which was seriously aggravated by the dusty milling environment which eventually killed him at the age of forty. His son-in-law, A S Palmer, said in an interview in 1964:

> The landlord ordered the mill to be pulled down. It was a terrible act of vandalism. The mill was in good condition and was possibly one of the best post-mills in the neighbourhood. I cannot give an exact year when it was demolished. It was a few years before William's death and he died in 1903.

A smock, Short's Mill (SU967062) was built here early in the nineteenth century – about 1820 says one source, 1827 another. It was damaged by a storm in 1887 and taken down in about 1896. This mill had replaced the earlier Willshears Mill which stood on the same site and burned down in 1809.

Washington

No trace remains of Old Mill, seen on maps of 1724 and 1753, and no documentary evidence exists.

Rock Mill (TQ128137), however, remains, albeit as a house conversion that was once the home of composer John Ireland. This was a black-tarred smock named for the rock on the east of Washington Common. It featured on maps between 1823 and 1920. It had a beehive cap and penthouse extension similar to that of Jolesfield Mill and this carried an eight-blade fan and a large set of one-and-a-half-shuttered patent sweeps. The sweeps powered two pairs of burrs and one of peaks.

The last miller was Henry Humphrey of Ashington, who also worked the Ashington watermill. Rock Mill ceased operating in 1905 and, still intact with sweeps and machinery, was eventually bought in 1919 by a Mr Redman to convert it into a house. The stocks were cut up to provide timber for bay windows and the central shaft was sawn into planks for use on the staircase. A small circular room with a gallery replaced the original cap.

Rock Mill when working

John Ireland (1879-1962) bought the property in 1954 and moved here from London to escape the street noise of Chelsea. The setting and the wonderful views are said to have inspired much of his music, including *Legend,* for piano and orchestra. But life at the mill was not harmonious for him. 'Now – the Bulldozer Symphony' was the headline in *The Evening News* of August 29, 1957. The report said:

> A cacophony of whirring machinery has brought a note of discord to the life of Dr. John Ireland, the composer. He stepped outside his 130-year-old converted windmill home on a picturesque hilltop at Washington, Sussex, to-day, and surveyed the scenery.
> His gaze took in the North and South Downs, with the famous

Cutting from The Evening News showing the windmill perched on the edge of the sandpit

beauty spot, Chanctonbury Ring. This was the countryside which inspired him to write "Amberley Wild Brooks".

He pointed below. "Look at those sandpits. It's shameful the way in which the countryside is being despoiled, and the noise from the machinery interrupts my studies."

Four years ago Dr. Ireland came to Rock Mill. The sandpits were there but were very much smaller and were hidden by bluebell woods.

'Shortly after he moved in, bulldozers began to extend the pits. Woodland dells where children used to play were swept away. Huge sand-washing machinery was installed, and blasting shook plaster from the mill's walls.

The windmill became almost encircled by sand-pits.

"From morning to dusk – and on Sundays some times – there's continuous noise," said the 78-year-old doctor. "Of course, the sand contractors are perfectly entitled to dig. They have leased the ground and have the mineral rights. But what a shame it is to destroy the countryside."

The house conversion seen in 1994

90

The work went on late into the evening and sometimes on Sundays and Ireland, driven to escape, took to sitting in the tranquil churchyard of St Mary the Virgin at Shipley. When he died in 1962 he was buried there, his grave being marked by sarsen stones.

Watersfield/Coldwaltham

Watersfield Common Mill stood on a ridge near Bury Gate and was marked on maps for only a relatively short time – between 1778 and 1813. Windmill Hill at Watersfield, Coldwaltham, is today's only reminder of a long-gone structure. A replacement, Watersfield Mill, was sited at the rear of the White Swallow Inn. In *Windmills in West Sussex* J P Paddon wrote:

> By a pleasant walk over Bury Hill, we passed on to Pulborough through Watersfield, which seems to have had a delightfully situated windmill of its own, from 1275 to 1869, although the one mentioned in very old records can scarcely have been the same as the post mill which is still in living memory.

Westbourne

Aldsworth Mill was marked on maps of 1778 and 1795. Nothing remains.

West Ashling

Here was a rare dual-powered mill, a tidal watermill surmounted by a windmill (SU808075). The watermill was a substantial brick building, some of its walls being 3ft thick, erected in 1825 for corn milling, although for a period it converted to a paper mill. The hollow windmill on the roof was put up in about 1860 by Hampshire millwrights Armfields, and between them the two mills drove six pairs of stones. The gearing was such that it could be worked by

West Ashling Windmill and Watermill in 1931

wind, water or steam. The hollow post mill had a sail-axle driving a centre shaft that passed through the roof.

In the 1920s an octogenarian told Thurston Hopkins that the windmill was put there in the year that the spire of Chichester Cathedral telescoped into the roof and fell into the choir, 'a disaster which the old fellow well remembered because he was a member of the choir at the time'. The steeple crashed on February 21, 1861. The windmill's sweeps were removed in 1916 but the fan remained until, in 1922, a neighbour complained about the noise of the wind in the fan mechanism and it, too, was removed. Remains of the windmill were dismantled in 1955.

West Chiltington

According to a post mortem inquisition into the death of Roger de Bavent on June 10, 1357, the windmill he had owned at Chyltyngton was in such a ruinous state that it was unworkable. But later it appears to have been rebuilt; in 1358 a Customal Roll for the Manor of Wiston assessed its annual work at six shillings and eightpence.

Chiltington Common Mill was an early smock windmill (dates vary from 1688 stated by artist Arthur Foord Hughes to around 1800; no true date has been established) built originally in the Monkmead area. This proved to be impractical in wet weather and the miller moved it about 1830 a mile and a half up the hill (TQ085181).

It was a black-tarred octagonal smock on a two-storey sandstone base and during its working days had its sweeps and fantail painted white. The mill drove three pairs of stones, and other machinery too.

At home in Meeten's Mill, 1937

In 1894 the mill was bought by Henry Meeten who worked it for twenty-eight years. Wrote Richard McDermott in *The Standing Windmills of West Sussex*:

> By virtue of his position as mill owner, and the importance of his Office (he was the last village Reeve) in the community life of the village, the windmill became acknowledged as Meeten's Mill, and his name once graced the VR post box set up at the corner of the land leading up to the mill.

In the 1920s, after it had fallen into disuse, the mill was bought by Major Hartley Clark, who lived opposite in a house called Fryars. He restored its structural timbers, put in central heating, floors, staircases, windows and all the then modern conveniences, making it into an unusual home. A contemporary description in *England of the Windmills* (1931) was:

> The ground floor is now an octagonal-shaped dining room with a

massive circular table around which are leather-covered round seats cut from the great wooden pillar. Above this is the drawing room with an exterior platform, and a gangway leading over the lane to a field. Above this are bedrooms looking out over Chanctonbury and the ridge of the South Downs. Right at the top is a small revolving attic whence you look out on one side to the axis of the sweeps and on the other to the fantail, which has a very large worm-geared wooden roller to control and retard the movement of the sails.

The ground floor dining room in 1930

West Dean

Binderton Rook Mill (or Rook Bindert's Mill), seen on maps between 1719 and 1753, was burned down and replaced by West Dean Mill. This was noted only on the maps of 1778 and 1779, and was known to have blown down. Then, replacing this one was mill number three, Rooks Hill Mill (TQ870109), on Rooks (or St Roche's) Hill. It featured on maps between 1795 and 1829.

West Hoathly

Brigden's Mill at West Hoathly was marked on only the map of 1800. It was located a mile and a half north-west of the church.

Wisborough Green

Kingett's Mill is a long-vanished windmill shown only on the map of 1795. Amblehurst Mill is another, shown only on the map of 1813. But much more remains of Wisborough Green's third mill, Champion's

Mill (TQ050258), a nineteenth century smock, the unusually tall two-storey sandstone base of which was converted into a house having four bedrooms and an octagonal living room.

This large white mill was built c1820. It had a domed cap which carried a fantail and spring sweeps which worked three pairs of stones and dressing machinery. At the end of the century the mill was also equipped with two pairs of engine-driven stones, making five pairs in all.

With trade lessening 'the windmill was allowed to become tail-winded in 1910'. But the sweeps became jammed

Champion's Mill in a state of dereliction, 1910

against the tower and Mr Champion, the owner, 'made a number of spectacular attempts to right the cap with men and ropes which only resulted in a good number of well-meaning folk being hurled into the air'.

Six months later the cap and sweeps were removed and the smock top was covered. In 1915 the smock was removed and the base roofed over. For many years the base was used as a store until the 1960s when it was sold and incorporated, complete with a replacement short smock, into a new house. Millstones were used to form an ornamental feature of the garden.

Champion's Mill in 1983: MLF

Wiston

There are early references here (1357-78) to Roger Wodeman's Mill.

East Wittering Mill in 1983: MLF

The Witterings

East Wittering Mill (SZ797973), sited just off the High Street, was built around 1810 and first marked on the 1813 OS map. It was worked with two spring and two common sweeps until 1880. The stones were a pair of burrs and a pair of peaks, underdriven.

The sweeps were removed in 1896 after one was broken when the brake was applied suddenly. The accident also damaged machinery. The cap blew off in 1931 and the interior fittings were destroyed by fire in 1975. The sturdy brick cone remains.

West Wittering Mill (SZ777980), seen on maps of 1724 and 1753, had gone by 1778.

Worth

Copthorne Post Mill (TQ335393) stood opposite the Duke's Head at Effingham according to map references between 1813 and 1823-61. It was burned down. Another, named Crawley Down Mill, and noted only on an 1800 map, was opposite the police station. This, too, has gone.

Worthing

At one time or another Worthing supplied work for nine windmills – although not simultaneously. The very earliest was one mentioned in the Palmere-Coverte survey undertaken in 1587 to discover which parts of the coast needed additional defences for the expected attack by Spain. The reference was:

> ... and between Little Hampton and Shoreham gode landinge for the moste parte, as at Kingston Stade so to Goringe Beacons, and therefore to be flancked and trenched. And in like sorte notwithstandinge that there is good landinge between these Beacons and Shoreham yet the coaste is reasonably well guarded viz. between Goringe and Heinde (Heene) Mille with a water between the Beache and the firme land save only next the mille and that muddy and growen with sedges.

A later mill was built nearby, or perhaps even on the same site, and this was known as Heene Mill (TQ129027). A post mill, it survived for some 200 years, and was seen on maps between 1724 and 1875. Apart from the maps, the earliest reference to this mill was in 1825 when a boy was struck by lightning while sheltering inside during a

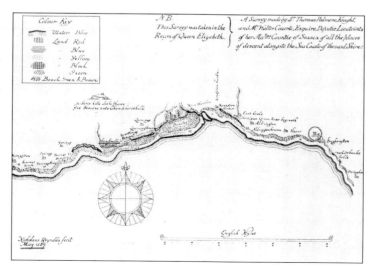

The map that accompanied the survey by Sir Thomas Palmere and Sir William Coverte in 1587. The old mill is seen circled to the right

Heene Mill as it was in 1884

thunderstorm. It was no longer working by 1893, when the last owner – baker Charles Botting – died and for ten years it stood unoccupied, with its sails intact, until it was demolished in 1903. The photograph below shows a new house being built in the grounds of the old black-painted mill, the workmen posing proudly with their tools.

Cross Street Mill came next and was the only windmill actually within the boundary of the hamlet of Worthing. It was another post mill that drove two pairs of stones and was capable of grinding four loads a week. It was seen on maps between 1823-61 and 1875 and was also known as Worthing Mill and Teville Mill. In 1805 an eight-year-old boy, Richard Cook, was struck by one of the sweeps while playing around the mill, and killed.

The mill was last used at this site in 1877 and on August 31 and September 1 of that year was moved out of town by Edward Isted. He

Heene Mill c1900

98

Cross Street Mill is seen in this John Nixon sketch of the Teville tollgate. To the right is the spire of West Tarring church and to the left, just visible on the horizon, is Highdown Mill

left no record of why he did so. The intended site at Seamills (whose name indicated that a mill or mills previously existed there) already had the two Navarino mills. Perhaps it was because, at the time, there were six or possibly seven mills in town, and he felt he could attract more trade on the rural fringe. The mill was dismantled by Edward Collins, its machinery, millstones, windshaft, sweeps and trestle were taken on ahead, leaving the body to be jacked up on to a trolley and

Before the move Cross Street Mill had Worthing Central Station as a neighbour

99

dragged by two teams of twenty horses each down Teville Road, Chapel Road and North Street to the High Street, knocking down only one lamp post on the way. The procession was cheered by massed spectators. But at the turn into Lyndhurst Road one team continued down the High Street while the other turned, leaving the mill stuck firmly on the corner. Haulage contractor Charles Poland, owner of the horses, unhitched his animals, packed up and went home. So did the spectators, leaving the mill there overnight.

George Trufitt's drawing of Cross Street Mill on the move

Meanwhile Mr Isted sought help from a Mr Holloway of Shoreham, who had recently invested in the very latest steam traction engine, and who was persuaded to turn up the next day to finish the job. The news flashed around town and retired architect George Trufitt was ready with his pad and pencil to record the thrilling scene. The great engine arrived, driven by Mr Holloway in a stovepipe hat. He hitched up the mill and set off for its new home. After the move the mill became known as Isted's Mill or, by some, as Sea Mill. It continued to work until 1892 and was demolished in 1903 – although according to Sam Clarke, a Worthing saddler speaking in an interview in 1955, the mill was moved again, this time to Nutbourne near Pulborough. This seems unlikely given that the old Cross Street Mill had stood derelict for a decade and was marked as disused on the 1901 Ordnance Survey.

The 1823-61 map shows a mill known as Seamill (TQ162031) of which nothing remains.

The two Navarino mills – North Mill and South Mill – existed east of the town, on the west side of Ham Road, from the early years of the eighteenth century, but were not marked on any maps after 1899. They were the finest of the town's mills, and the last to be pulled down. North Mill was the older, having been built some time between 1800 and 1813 for Richard Hide and first known as Hide's Mill or East Mill. Contemporary records described it as a smock mill but in fact it was a four-storeyed octagonal tower mill constructed of red brick. It had four common sweeps working two pairs of stones, and a fan, this arrangement later being changed to two common and two spring sweeps.

South Mill, known as Newland's Navarino Mill, was built some time between 1827 and 1831 by millwright James Sheppard (who had also built the first house in the district and called it Navarino after the sea battle of 1827 in which the combined fleets of Britain, France and Russia defeated those of Turkey and Egypt), for Sompting farmer and corn merchant, George Newland. It was a large, five-storied tower mill fitted with shuttered sweeps that worked two pairs of stones and was capable of grinding six loads of grain a week. In its later years the millstones were steam-driven via pulley. George Newland died in 1862 and left the mill to his son Robert, who went on to acquire North

The Navarino tower mills that stood at the south end of Ham Road

Mill as well, naming the pair of them the Navarino Mills. Then when Robert died in 1887 the mills, together with the High Street corn merchant's premises, passed to his nephew William Barker, who continued to work the mills until his death in 1896. By 1900 the two mills were without work and fell into disuse. North Mill was taken down in 1902 and South Mill was demolished in 1910 to make way for residential development.

Broadwater Mill in decay, c1914

Broadwater Mill, also known as Cissbury Mill, Warren Farm Mill, Ballard's Mill and Offington Mill (TQ139060), was another post type, seen on maps from 1780 to 1909. It was sited on the slope of Mount Carvey, a southern projecting spur of Cissbury. An early miller was a Mr Patching who worked it in 1750 (preceding the earliest map reference by thirty years); his son, William Patching, was apprenticed to Edward Hide, builder, brother of the North Navarino Mill's Richard Hide. This partnership of Hide and Patching eventually developed into the Worthing estate agency of Patching and Co.

During the middle and latter part of the nineteenth century Broadwater Mill was worked by Charles Ballard, hence one of its alternative names. Ballard took part in the early exploration of the Cissbury flint mines with Colonel Lane Fox (later General Pitt Rivers) and Canon Greenwell in 1867-68.

It was by all accounts a fine old post mill which fell into disuse after its working life was over by 1901 and, instead of being cared for as an embellishment to the landscape, it was left to decay. Eventually it was pulled down and its timbers sold to firewood merchants in the early days of the First World War. Worthing Golf Links now covers the site.

Another Worthing mill, also gone, was an unnamed flour mill seen on the 1875 OS map on a site coinciding with the north end of Heatherstone Road. Very little is known about this mysterious mill, but it may have been the North Heath Mill of Pulborough which was said to have been bought by a Mr Booker, dismantled and moved to Worthing in 1874. Legend has it that the mill was taken apart by the 'William Foard Tribe' and that the mill was known as Tribe's Folly.

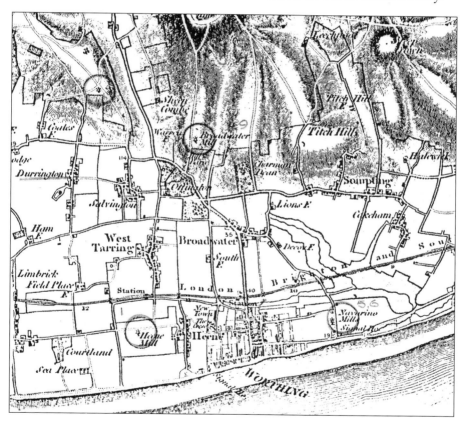

Reprint of the OS map of 1813, showing Heene Mill to the west of Worthing, the two Navarino mills to the east and Broadwater (Cissbury) Mill to the north

BIBLIOGRAPHY

Austen, Brian: *Windmills of Sussex*, Sabre Publishing 1978
Batten, M I: *English Windmills, Vol I*, Architectural Press 1930
Beckett, Arthur: *Adventures of a Quiet Man*, Combridges 1933
Beedell, Susan: *Windmills* 1975
Betjeman, John: *Victorian and Edwardian Brighton*, Batsford 1974
Bennett, Richard and Elton, John: *History of Corn Milling*, Simpkin Marshall 1898-1904
Brangwyn, Frank and Preston, Hayter: *Windmills*, John Lane 1923
Brunnarius, Martin: *Windmills of Sussex*, Phillimore 1979
Cheal, Henry: *The Story of Shoreham*, S R Publishers 1971
de Candole, Henry: *The Story of Henfield*, Combridges, 1947
Fleming, Lindsay: *History of Pagham*, Ditchling Press 1949
Fowell, G M and Hughes, A Foord: *Windmills in Sussex*, Walkers Galleries 1930
Ham, Joan: *Storrington in Pictures*
Hemming, the Rev Peter: *Windmills in Sussex*, C W Daniels 1936
Hopkins, R Thurston: *Old English Mills and Inns*, Cecil Palmer 1927
   Old Watermills and Windmills, Phillip Allan 1931, *Windmills*, Charles Clarke
Long, George: *The Mills of Man*, Herbert Joseph 1931
Lower, M A: *A Compendious History of Sussex*
Mais, S P B: *England of the Windmills*, Dent 1931
McDermott, Richard and Richard: *The Standing Windmills of West Sussex* 1978
Paddon, J P: *Windmills in West Sussex*, Oxford 1925
Price, Bernard: *Sussex People, Places, Things*, Phillimore 1975
Simmons H E S: *Sussex Windmill Survey*
Snewin, E and Smail, H: *Worthing Pageant – Glimpses of Old Worthing* 1945
Swinfen, Warden and Arscott, David: *Hidden Sussex*, BBC Books 1984
Littlehampton, The Official Guide 1926
Shoreham, Southwick and Steyning, Homeland Handbook, 1907

Magazines and newspapers

Country Life
Sussex County Magazine
Sussex Life
Chichester Observer
Littlehampton News
Sussex Weekly Advertiser

Sussex Daily News
The Daily Telegraph
The Evening News
The Times
West Sussex Gazette

GLOSSARY

Angle of weather: the twist of the sweep from 4° to 22°

Auxiliary drive: a power-take-off system for dressing and cleaning equipment

Base: the brick structure supporting a smock mill

Bedstone: the lower, fixed millstone

Bell alarm: warning operated when the feed hopper is empty

Bin: the wooden container for grain, meal or flour

Bin floor: the floor where the grain bins are kept

Body: upper part of a post or smock mill

Bolter: meal dresser

Brake: the sections of wood strapped together around the brake wheel to stop the mill from working

Brake lever: a beam of iron or timber that applied the braking load

Brake rope: the cord attached to the brake lever

Brake catch: latching iron that held the brake off

Brake screw: mechanism devised by Holloway for applying the brake in tower mills

Brake wheel: Main windshaft wheel in smock and tower mills or the head wheel of a post mill.

Bran: skin of grain taken as tailings from the dresser

Breast: area of the working face of a millstone between the eye and the skirt; also the front wall of a post mill's body

Breast beam: baulk of timber that supports the neck of the windshaft at the front of the mill

Burr stone: a freshwater quartz from the Paris basin in France

Canister: iron casting through which the stocks pass at the front of the windshaft

Cant post: main upright corner timbers in a smock mill

Canvas: cloth or common sail material

Cap: the top that rotates and carries the sweeps and windshaft on smock and tower mills.

Cap types: beehive, a domed cap resembling an old-style straw bee kep; bonnet or hooded, resembling an old-fashioned bonnet; ogee, a type of beehive with reverse curved pinnacle

Casing: wooden box surrounding the stones and supporting the feed assembly

Centre post: main vertical upright shaft of a post mill

Chute: feed channel from the grain bin to the hopper

Cleaning machine: used for removing dirt, husks and chaff from the grain

Common sweep: earliest form that had canvas spread over the framework

Composition stone: man-made from carborundum and cement frit

Cross trees: the timbers that support a post mill trestle

Crown tree: the timber baulk that crowns the centre post and supports the whole weight of a post mill body

Crusher: roller mill used for crushing oats

Cubitt, William: the man who patented automatic sweep striking gear

Damsel: agitating device in grain feed mechanism

Dead sails: common sweep frames or modern reproduction sweeps

Derbyshire stone: hard sandstone from the Peak District

Dresser: centrifugal machine for grading meal into flour, offals and bran

Dresser floor: separate floor for the dressing and cleaning machinery

Dressing: (1) grading meal into flour, offals and bran; (2) pattern of lands, furrows and cracking on the working surface of a millstone; (3) re-sharpening millstones

Drift: Sussex term for the set or angle of weather of sweeps

Elliptical spring: device used to control spring sweeps

Eye: central aperture of the millstone

Fan: winding gear on a tail pole of a post mill or the cap of a smock or tower mill

Fan blade: wooden segment set at 150° to the fan axis

Fan spindle: iron shaft carrying the fan assembly

Fan staging: platform at the rear of a cap on smock and tower mills to provide access to the fan-tail

Feathering: light narrow grooving between millstone furrows

Feed: general term for grist or animal fodder

Feed Line: hemp string that controls the setting of the feed shoe

French burr: millstone composed of segments of freshwater quartz held in plaster of Paris and bound with iron hoops

Furrow: main radial grooves on the millstone face

Gallery: staging around smock and tower mills at spout floor level giving access to the sweeps

Gear floor: between the cap and bin floors, housing wallower and sack hoist

Governor: mechanism comprising weights and lever arms for controlling stone tentering, ie the gap between the stones

Grain: seed of barley, oats and wheat

Great spur wheel: large gear at the bottom of the upright shaft that transmits the drive to the stone nuts in smock and tower mills

Head: part of a post mill body forward of the main post

Head stones: pair of stones in a post mill driven by the brake wheel

Head wheel: forward windshaft wheel in a post mill

Heel: inner end of a sweep

Hemlath: leading outer rail of a common sweep

Horizontal shaft: take-off drive

Kibbler: crushing machine

Lands: flat areas on the face of millstones between furrows

Layshaft: auxiliary drive shaft

Leading edge: front edge of a sweep

Meikle, A: inventor of the spring sweep

Multure: toll taken by the miller in meal

Nether stone: the bed stone

Open trestle mill: post mill without a roundhouse

Overdrift: method of driving millstones from above

Patent sweeps: shuttered sweeps controlled by Cubitt's weight and chain method

Peak stones: millstones cut from sandstone from the Derbyshire Peak district

Pintle: spindled end of a centre post that runs in a bearing

Poll end: morticed end of a windshaft carrying the stocks

Pollards: coarse flour and fine bran taken from the third spout of a dresser

Post: main vertical shaft of a post mill

Quant: drive spindle to upper stone in an overdrive arrangement
Quern: hand-operated mill
Roundhouse: masonry or timber base enclosing a post mill trestle
Runner stone: upper stone of a pair
Sack flap: upward opening trap doors in mill floors
Sack hoist: pulley system for raising sacks of grain within the mill
Sail: sweep
Sail cloth: canvas spread and furled on common sweep frames
Seconds: larger particles of coarse flour from the dresser's second spout
Shoe: feed trough to direct the grain from the hopper into the eye of the runner stone
Shutter: pivoted wooden slat in sails
Spider: device that opens or closes shutters in patent sails/sweeps
Spout floor: beneath the stones where the newly ground meal is delivered
Spring sweeps: individually controlled shuttered sweeps
Spur gear: straight-toothed gear or pinion
Spur gear mill: post mill with underdrift stones driven via a wallower and spur gear
Staging: gallery
Stock: timber that supports the sweeps
Sweep: Sussex word for sail
Swift: Sussex word for cloth-covered or common sweep
Tackle: mill machinery
Tail: part of a post mill body behind the centre post
Tail beam: timber supporting the tail bearing of a windshaft
Tail bearing: bearing at the tail end of a windshaft
Tail pole: long timber lever for winding a post mill
Tail wheel: driving wheel at the tail end of a windhsaft
Tail-winded: situation in which the wind is on the back of the sweeps
Tailings: bran and coarse flour particles
Talthur: lever used for raising the steps on early post mills
Tentering: the setting of the gap between millstones
Thirds: pollards
Trestle: timber supporting frame of a post mill

Trolley steps: ladder of a post mill mounted on truck wheels when a fantail is used
Underdrift: method of driving millstones from below
Wallower: bevel wheel used for taking the drive from a brake wheel
Weather: twist built into a sweep to give it driving power
Weathering: streamlining or fairing of the mill to encourage windflow
Windshaft: main driving shaft from which all windmill machinery is operated
Winnower: cleaning machine to remove chaff and dirt etc from the grain before grinding

APPENDIX

Maps on which West Sussex mill sites are shown

1579 Christopher Saxton's map of Sussex, Surrey, Kent and Middlesex
1587 A survey of the coast of Sussex made by two deputy lieutenants, Sir Thomas Palmer and Sir William Covert, to see what parts required additional sea defences against the threatened invasion from Spain. It was published by Mark Anthony Lower in 1870
1610 John Speed's map of Sussex
1727 Richard Budgen's map of Sussex shows fifty mill sites
1795 Yeakell and Gardner. *The Great Survey* in four sheets
1813 This is the usually quoted date of the first Ordnance Survey map. A total of six sheets, covering the entire county, were published between 1810 and 1819 and they show 153 windmill sites
1825 Charles and John Greenwood's map of Susssex

ACKNOWLEDGMENTS

In his files Maurice Lawson Finch listed those he wished to thank for their generous help and assistance in his windmill researches. In respect of West Sussex mill sites they were: Frank Gregory, Stella Palmer, R C Reynolds, Mr and Mrs Slade of Beech Farm, Whitemans Green, Mary Taylor of Rustington, Alan Davis of Nutbourne, Dr George Shaw of Lancing College, J S Gray.

He also wished to thank H E Catt, librarian of the RAC, Pall Mall; H G Clark of Rustington Library, staff of Worthing Library and the staff of West Sussex Record Office.

Eileen Finch wishes to thank the following for checking facts and for bringing the story of standing West Sussex mills up to date: Peter Hill, chairman of the Sussex Mills Group, and chairman of the Friends of West Blatchington Mill; Simon Potter of Jill Mill; Jim Woodward-Nutt of Shipley Mill; Philip Higgs of Oldland Mill; Bob Potts, Pete Casebow and Roger Ashton of High Salvington Mill.

PICTURE CREDITS

Wherever the information is available pictures are individually credited. Many of the postcards give no details of the publisher.

WINDMILLS AT WORK IN EAST SUSSEX

Compiled by Brigid Chapman
from the research material of the late
MAURICE LAWSON FINCH